# Layman's Guide to

# $ Oil & Gas Investments

## Thomas E. Brown

Gulf Publishing Company
Book Division
Houston, London, Paris, Tokyo

Layman's Guide to
# Oil & Gas Investments

## Library of Congress Cataloging in Publication Data

Brown, Thomas Edward, 1932-
  Layman's guide to oil & gas investments.

  Bibliography: p.
  Includes index.
    1. Petroleum industry and trade—United States—Finance.    2. Gas,
Natural—United States—Finance.
I. Title.    II. Title: Oil & gas investments.
HD9565.B76                          332.6'722                          81-4968
ISBN 0-87201-344-8                                                      AACR2

# Acknowledgments

In the preparation of this study the writer relied heavily on the good graces of friends who are professionals in their own fields. They have demonstrated exceptional patience in attempting to correct various technical misconceptions that sometimes entered the manuscript. The inadequate treatment of any subject matter, all ambiguities, and errors or omissions should be duly credited to the writer. The real experts are acknowledged in alphabetical order:

Louis H. Barnett
Jim C. Bell
Burke Burkart
John C. Harvey
S. Erik Johnston
Alden B. McCall
Duane M. McDaniel
Steve McGinnis
Donald L. Parnell
David S. Pressley
Fred W. Rabalais
Kurt A. Webber

Special appreciation is extended to Ms. Becky Renfro and Ms. Kenya Yates for typing and editing on all preliminary drafts of the manuscript.

# Dedication

To Jean, Cindy, Liz, Sarah, Tom, Titus, and Adam.

# Contents

 # Preface

Investment in an oil or gas enterprise is an adventure that requires only money and trust. Knowledge of the subject is not an *essential* ingredient—its only value lies in reducing the investment risk and improving the profit potential.

The purpose of this guide is to assist the "unsophisticated" oil and gas investor and to present some guidelines for survival in "dangerous waters." One mean alligator can eat a lot of fish.

Laws relating to securities transactions require that an investor in an oil or gas venture involving *unregistered securities* be either sophisticated in the investment concern or have a knowledgeable representative who is qualified to pass judgment on the technical merit of the investment. This requisite, categorized as a *Safe Harbor Benefit,* must be met before an organization can sell unregistered securities.

One of several definitions of sophistication, according to Webster, is to be "deprived of native or original simplicity." The federal courts interpret sophistication as a demonstrable level of experience, and the ability to formulate meaningful questions pertinent to the proposed investment.

Small-investor oil and gas deals are usually accompanied by an *offering circular* which outlines the business terms and includes a geological discussion of the prospect. Commonly, a statement will preface the circular in which the investor will attest to his wisdom in the oil and gas business:

> "This private offering circular is number _____ of a limited number of counterparts thereof prepared by _____ for certain *sophisticated, qualified* investors selected by it. This offering circular is for the exclusive use of _____ and does not constitute an offer to sell interests to, or a solicitation of a purchase offer from, any other person. Reproduction of this offering circular in whole or in part is absolutely prohibited."

By a stroke of the pen (on a check), *exit* original simplicity, *enter* sophistication. Pandora's box is opened, and footfalls are heard on a well-trod path into a combat zone where prisoners are seldom taken.

The first fraudulent oil deal that this writer had an opportunity to analyze involved a friend several years ago. The victim in this instance was an M.D. who displayed a touching amount of trust in an individual who likely lies about his marital status at church picnics. The outcome of the venture was a minor setback in the investors long-term financial goals, and the development of a more callous outlook in appraising subsequent oil or gas ventures.

An oil or gas deal directed to an individual in a non-oil-related profession should routinely be stamped with the following legend: *Caution.* Oil and gas investments are always heady and are sometimes toxic.

As this book is designed to assist the part-time oilman, the variety and permutations of deals between consenting professionals will only be lightly discussed. These are the heavyweights who fight their own battles, alone or in concert with legions of technical experts. Theirs is "trench warfare" where data are reviewed, analyzed, discussed, and possibly demeaned. Ridiculous offers may be parried with insulting counter offers. When the smoke has cleared, and a deal has been agreed upon, the professionals separate with each side believing themselves the victors. In this type of confrontation experience rules the game, and there are no apologies or excuses for the ultimate outcome of the venture. A costly decision is made with the net result being either success or another dry hole that is sometimes labeled a "monument to science."

From the day the drillpipe "starts turning to the right" on a well, the investor lives a Walter Mitty existence, fantasizing how to spend his anticipated wealth. With a little success, he will be an oilman, and with great success, an oil baron. He has joined the ranks of the "wildcatters" and is pitting his wits and his money in a high-stake game where the losers outnumber the winners. It's *macho* to invest and Superman to win.

Regrettably, "the thrill of victory and the agony of defeat" are not on par. To the investor, success is the expected and thus carries no surprises. Conversely, a *junked* or *plugged* well (these terms relate to mechanical problems and exploration failures, respectively) can be a sobering experience, with a person's degree of involvement dictating the advisability of self-destruction.

The search for oil and gas is a science that relies largely on the talents of professionals and the techniques and instrumentation they employ. It is not an exact science, as the preponderance of dry holes to successful oil or gas wells attests. One rumor, probably initiated by petroleum engineers and spread by land-men, darkly suggests that petroleum geologists have green and yellow darts they throw at land maps for the location of oil or gas prospects. If this story were indeed true, the success of "exploratory wildcat" wells would probably hover below 1% rather than at the plump 10-20% now enjoyed.

In any general discussion of oil and gas ventures the three most popular topics are success, luck, and fraud. The three themes, although real, are highly overrated. Success (usually someone else's) is the lure to the investor. Luck can only be good; bad events can generally be traced to some real factor, such as inadequate data, faulty equipment, incompetent management, or an uneconomic deal. Fraud is present in only a minor percentage of oil and gas investments as a calculated plan. Most losses result from a compounding of wasteful and inept management.

An often-repeated yarn with a strong factual basis centers on a drilling rig move where a wagon or truck (depending on the vintage of the story) breaks down, leaving the equipment stranded. Various factors enter the picture and dictate that a well be drilled at the site of the breakdown. Geologists, with tear-streaked faces, plead and threaten in an attempt to have the drilling order rescinded. But the well is drilled, and the Black Gold Mother Lode Bonanza Field is discovered. The usual conclusion to this tale is that had the rig reached its proposed site it not only would have drilled a dry hole but would have been cursed forever for desecrating an Apache burial ground.

Oilmen are quick to point out that, unlike gold and silver, which frequently are disposed to wait patiently for discovery, oil and gas are vagabonds with patterns of movement over millions of years that are controlled by forces within the earth. A slogan for the frustrated searcher might be "where it was ain't necessarily where it is or maybe it is where it was, sometimes."

Fortunately, there are rules (frequently obscure) that oil and gas must obey and that the explorationist must understand. It is the comprehension of these rules and the ability and willingness to employ the necessary exploration tools that separate the oil finders from "Dusty" or "Dry Hole Charlies." Success in the oil business is the development of enough profit with any single discovery to counterbalance the succession of dry holes that even the most talented oil finders experience.

Failure is an unwelcome but common companion to oil investors. Oil companies and wealthy individuals possess the resources to enter into a diversity of programs and to "ride out" a series of reversals. Many small investors, on the other hand, must either "hit" on their first venture or retire from the arena. Any professional gambler can verify the comfort of adequate resources that enable him to ride out a series of "bad cards."

Let the reader be warned that the sole purpose of this presentation is to provide a foundation for minimizing the emotional approach to oil investments. There is room for sanity and clear-thinking in all oil deals.

# Chapter One

# $ The Product

The attraction of oil, unlike gold or silver, is not its physical appearance. A tar necklace or asphalt dinner service would be impractical and messy. Likewise, the search for oil does not carry the romantic image of a gold prospector and his burro, wandering through endless waste, seeking the mother lode. The charm of oil is not in what it is, but rather what it can do. Oil is money and money is power. As long as oil remains essential to the economy, fortunes will be made by those who find and exploit it.

Oil and gas are considered in various lights, depending on the perspective of the viewer. To an investor in a variety of drilling ventures, it's legalized gambling with house rules changing from prospect to prospect as deals are varied and chances of success fluctuate. To the explorationists and rig workers concerned with finding oil, it's a job that can be either satisfying or disheartening, depending on the outcome of a venture. A good discovery well will inflate wallets, expand egos, and widen the oil finder's circle of friends. Conversely, a dry and abandoned well is quickly forgotten . . . except by bank loan officers who maintain close communication with the would-be oil finder.

1

## What Is Oil?

As found in nature, oil is a mixture of organic compounds, collectively called *hydrocarbons,* that have carbon and hydrogen as their elemental constituents. These hydrocarbons are grouped on the basis of their ratio of hydrogen to carbon and the nature of the linkage between the two elements. Figure 1-1 shows the simple hydrocarbon molecule for methane.

It is thought that oil is formed under high temperatures and pressures, normally associated with the parent organic matter being buried many thousands of feet beneath the earth's surface. To achieve this burial depth, a time passage of several millions of

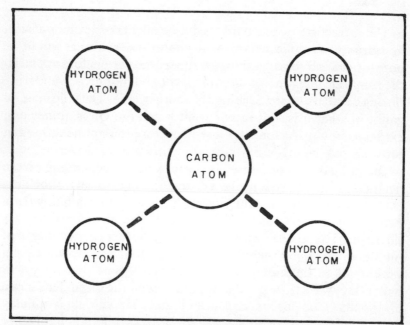

**Figure 1-1**—Four hydrogen atoms are bonded to one carbon atom to form a methane (hydrocarbon) molecule. (From: *Introduction to Petroleum Production,* Vol. 1, D.R. Skinner, Gulf Pub. Co., 1981.)

years is required. This estimation is based on the acceptance that geological events in the past are correctly interpreted on the evidence of contemporary observations and experimentation.

Crude oil (unrefined oil) may be green, black, brown, or yellow in color, and greenish overtones are common. It is, by definition, a liquid at the earth's surface at standard temperatures and pressures.

(In the words of Hardrock Burke, gold prospector and desert rat, "Oil, hell! It might slosh on your boots, but it sure won't jingle in your pockets. Everyone knows if you sniff the fumes you'll see green and act simple.")

In a deeply buried reservoir hydrocarbons commonly exist as a liquid, but when exposed to lower pressure such as at the earth's surface, it may either remain a liquid or convert to gas, depending on its composition. Conversely, in some buried reservoirs the hydrocarbon may exist as a gas and either remain a gas or convert to a liquid when brought to the surface. There is an interrelationship between temperature, pressure, and hydrocarbon composition that determines its physical state at different burial depths.

Hydrocarbons are found in nature either as solids, liquids, or gases. The solid hydrocarbons, commonly called *bitumens,* exhibit no liquid characteristics under standard temperature and pressure conditions. Large deposits of bitumens have been found in various parts of the world. In the past bitumen extraction from deep reservoirs has been too costly for commercialization.

*Tar sands* and *oil shales* are presently receiving great attention because of their potential to yield usable petroleum products. A *tar sand* is a sand body containing a very thick or viscous form of oil where the lighter and more volatile constituents have been removed. Large deposits of tar sands are known to occur at or near the earth's surface, which permits strip mining. The initial development and accumulation of these hydrocarbons probably took place at great depths in the earth, resulting from continued burial and transformation of large quantities of organic material. The erosion of the overlying rocks has exposed this material at the surface in many areas. Contact with water or air has effected the removal of the lighter hydrocarbons and concentrated the heavier components as a tar-like substance.

The petroleum potential of oil shale is enormous because of the large quantity of this rock exposed at or near the earth's surface. An efficient and economic extraction of petroleum from these shales could result in a much brighter economic picture for oil in the next century. Shale is a rock composed primarily of clay and silt-size material. It is characterized by low *porosity* (pore space or voids) and virtually no *permeability* (the ability of fluids to flow through the rock). Oil shales are believed to originate in an environment where muds high in organic matter were deposited. Subsequent burial of these muds to great depths in the earth resulted in the conversion of the organic matter to hydrocarbons. The oil was trapped in the minute pores of the shale because of its inability to pass through this impermeable body. Several major energy-oriented corporations are presently studying techniques to economically extract the hydrocarbons from these shale bodies.

Oil is found in the pore spaces of various rock types and is nearly always associated with both natural gas and water. A large area or field from which oil is produced is frequently called an *oil pool*. This terminology has led to the misconception by some people that oil is found in underground lakes or rivers, rather than its normal occurrence within very small openings (pores) in different rock bodies.

A very light, volatile oil is called a condensate. In behavior and appearance it is similar to gasoline. Condensates are the common associate of natural gas.

The terms *sweet* and *sour* are frequently applied to crude oils. They designate the oil's sulfur content. Low-sulfur, or sweet crudes (less than 0.5% by weight of sulfur compounds), are more desirable for refining purposes than are sour crudes.

In the United States crude oil is commonly measured in barrels (42 U.S. gallons) and is generally categorized by its *gravity*, in degrees API. The formula for determining degrees API gravity is:

$$API = (141.5 \div \text{specific gravity of}$$
$$\text{oil sample at } 60° \text{ F}) - 131.5$$

Specific gravity is the weight of a substance compared to the weight of an equal volume of water. Therefore, the specific gravity of water is 1, and its degree API gravity is 10. The heavier and thicker an oil, the lower its degree API gravity. Conversely, light oils and condensates have high-degree API gravity values.

## What Is Natural Gas?

The term "natural gas," as commonly used, refers to the four primary constituents of the paraffin group of hydrocarbons. These four members, listed in order of increasing weight and molecular complexity, are methane, ethane, propane, and butane. Under normal temperature and pressure conditions as found at the surface of the earth, they exist as gases. The remaining members of the paraffin series (pentane, hexane, heptane, octane, etc.) exist as liquids under standard temperature and pressure conditions. Methane is the only hydrocarbon that will always be present in a natural gas. Non-hydrocarbon gases commonly found in association with natural gases are carbon dioxide, helium, hydrogen sulfide, and nitrogen.

A natural gas is labeled "dry" if it has no companion liquid hydrocarbons. A "wet" gas is one that includes some condensate (highly volatile liquids that have a high-degree API gravity).

Natural gas is usually measured in cubic feet. A large quantity is expressed in thousands of cubic feet (Mcf). A million cubic feet is MMcf, and a million cubic feet per day is MMcfgpd.

When a reservoir produces both gas and oil, a gas-oil ratio is determined. This relationship is the ratio of the cubic feet of gas to the barrels of oil being produced at a particular time.

Within an oil and gas reservoir, the natural gas can occur as either a cap (a discrete zone in a rock body in which the pore spaces contain gas and which overlies a zone in which the pore

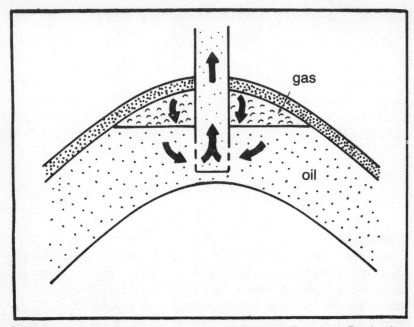

**Figure 1-2a**—Gas cap drive. (From: *Introduction to Petroleum Production*, Vol. 1, D.R. Skinner, Gulf Pub. Co., 1981.)

spaces contain oil) or in solution in the oil. When a well penetrates the reservoir, the gas expands because of the drop in pressure and forces oil to the surface. This type of drive mechanism is referred to as either solution gas or gas cap drive, depending on the occurrence of the gas. Oil recovery from an oil reservoir with a gas-drive mechanism is generally less efficient than in a water-drive oil reservoir. (See Figures 1-2a and 1-2b.)

## How Are Oil and Gas Formed?

This question has been discussed and argued for many years. Some arguments favor an inorganic origin, a recitation of circumstances where hydrocarbons are believed to be found in the absence of organic life. The occurrence of methane in association

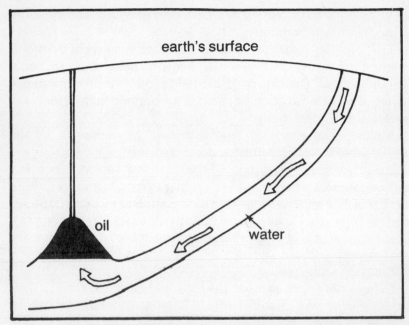

**Figure 1-2b**—Bottom water drive. (From: *Introduction to Petroleum Production,* Vol. 1, D.R. Skinner, Gulf Pub. Co., 1981.)

with volcanic eruptions, and its apparent presence in the atmosphere of other planets in the solar system, strongly indicates that organic life, as known on earth, is not a requisite for its development. Methane is the principal component of nearly all natural hydrocarbon gases and is usually a common associate of oil, a mixture of more complex hydrocarbons.

However, it is widely accepted by petroleum geologists and other earth scientists that all oil and gas deposits, both produced and sought, were formed from organic remains. This plant and animal debris is believed to have accumulated under protective conditions (away from the earth's atmosphere, where the oxygen could not destroy the organic material) and continually buried deeper by sediments, it transformed into petroleum. This change in the organic matter is not completely understood, but it appears to be a result of increasing temperature, pressure, and possibly some chemical effects.

The organic material is thus ultimately converted into a mixture of liquid and gaseous hydrocarbons and, in some instances, coal. The nature of the final product is now popularly assumed to be a function of the type of organic matter that was present before the change.

Anyone who studies a coal seam will be impressed by the abundance of leaf imprints and other plant fragments that are frequently visible. The origin of coal is thus assumed to occur in an environment where plant life proliferated and conditions were such that this material was able to accumulate in vast quantities and without destruction by atmospheric oxygen or destructive organisms. A swamp is such an environment and, for most known coal deposits, these swamps or marshes would have existed millions of years ago.

Oil and gas do not provide the readily identifiable clues to their origin which coal generously offers. Laboratory studies have been conducted for years in an attempt to provide a direct association between petroleum and many suspect parents. The most popular opinion, backed by a large amount of substantiating data, is that both plant and animal organisms have contributed to the formation of both oil and gas. These organisms and their components were commonly of a very fine or microscopic size and inhabited the seas or submerged land areas (swamps, marshes, estuaries) adjoining the seas. Great quantities of organic matter were also transported by rivers and streams from land areas and likely provided a significant percentage of hydrocarbon source material.

One popular explanation why natural gas is frequently found with no associated oil is that natural gas is an end-product of land-derived organic matter, and oil is an end-product of ocean-derived organic matter. Another explanation for many natural gas occurrences is that high temperatures have caused oil to break down into the less complex gases. Temperature increases with depth into the earth, and thus there are depths beyond which oil cannot survive. The stability range for natural gas extends considerably beyond these depths. For this reason, the continued development of deeper drilling activities will ultimately result in the establishment of more natural gas reserves but will contribute little to primary oil recovery.

The basins in which the organic material was initially accumulated, along with various sediments, were mostly situated along ancient coastlines or in shallow seas. Constantly changing conditions over large spans of geologic time have frequently allowed these basins to grow in size and increase in depth. As rock, mineral, and organic debris continued to accumulate in a basin, the underlying material was compressed from this added weight and the basin slowly began to sink. Liquids (water and oil) and gases were pushed out as the weight of the overlying rocks and sediments increased. Commonly, these liquids and gases, under high pressure, migrated to areas of less pressure and displaced other fluids in their path. This movement continued until the fluids either came to the surface (oil and gas seeps) or approached a barrier that stopped their movement.

This barrier that commonly stops the movement of oil or gas, or even water, is designated a *trap*. The explorationist is seeking this trap, since it is here that oil and gas frequently accumulate in large quantities.

## How Are Oil and Gas Found?

"You take this forked creosote branch, dip it in your car's gas tank, and then walk around the property. When that stick starts quivering and then noses down, well then you know you got a humdinger. . . ."

The search for oil and gas has been a continuous learning process that has followed a winding trail littered with empty billfolds. The evolution of search methods has had many setbacks and false starts. New techniques and "black boxes" will appear in the race and, after a decent trial period by some front runner, will frequently be left behind.

It's a meat and potato business where the only assurance of gaining weight is to stick to fundamentals and then to do it right. The basics of finding oil or gas are: (1) to restrict your search to regions where they are known to occur, (2) to understand the conditions that are necessary for their entrapment within the selected area, (3) to be prepared to employ all necessary technology in locating their habitat, and (4) to be willing to risk a large sum of money in drilling one or several wells.

The regions where large volumes of oil and gas have already been found are being continuously recycled in the search. These are established fairways that have a proven potential and, through the application of both improved knowledge and technology, will continue to yield new discoveries.

The mechanics of finding oil or gas are like a pyramid with an idea at the base and a test well at the apex. The in-between steps are the data and techniques the explorationist will employ in refining or rejecting the initial concept. A primary tool will be the collection and evaluation of all available information from wells that have been drilled in the region, including all production histories. These data will be analyzed in detail with maps and cross sections constructed to show the geologic relationship of the area under study to neighboring producing wells.

In the search for oil or gas it is essential that a trap be located, and that affiliated rocks have oil and gas storage capabilities as well as characteristics that allow recovery of the products. A trap is a zone in a rock body that has prevented the escape of gas or liquids to the earth's surface. It may be because of the presence of a dense (low permeability) rock that blocks the path of escaping fluids, allowing accumulations of hydrocarbons to build up. When the flow has ceased, there is a general separation of gas from oil and oil from water within the trap. This broad separation is caused by the density difference between the three substances. The gas rises to the top and overlies the oil, which in turn overlies the water. This trap, caused by a permeability difference between adjoining rocks, is called a *stratigraphic trap*. In general, this type of trapping mechanism is the most difficult to find as its definition requires a great deal of data, obtainable only from massive amounts of well information in the search area.

Many major and countless minor oil and gas fields are the result of stratigraphic traps, and many small-investor drilling programs are involved in this type of *play*, frequently because of the more moderate costs of locating drill sites as opposed to employing geophysical techniques. When the geologist has completed a study of this type, a map or series of maps will accompany his report which locates the proposed drill site and states the rationale for drilling. Characteristically, the report will indicate how effectively the assumed reservoir (the zone that contains the oil or gas) is bounded both above and, in part, laterally by a "tight" or impermeable zone through which the oil and gas cannot flow, and thus is trapped.

*Structural traps* differ from their stratigraphic counterparts by the localization of petroleum in geologic features (structures) which are broken or bent rock zones within the earth's crust. Geologists designate the bending and breaking of a rock body as *folding* and *faulting*, respectively. By bending a rock body, a crest or "high" is formed and a structural trap may result. Fluids squeezed out from compacting sediments are continuously moving, at very slow rates, through any rock body that is porous and permeable. As this movement progresses, there is continued redistribution of gas, oil, and water within the rock body through which these substances migrate. This fluid stream is restricted to movement within a permeable rock unit, and thus flow will continue laterally and upward or downward in a course paralleling the rock's boundaries. At the crest of any high point, the overlying pressure is less than in adjacent low areas, and thus a part of the fluid in the upper stream will accumulate at that point. In effect, a residue of oil and gas is left in the highs, with this residue continuing to accumulate over millions of years to form an oil or gas deposit.

A major advantage of a structural trap is that geophysical instruments (especially seismic) can frequently detect these highs and lows at depths of thousands and even tens of thousands of feet below the surface of the earth. Consequently, some information on the character and extent of a structural trap can be demonstrated prior to initiating a costly drilling program.

Geophysical surveys are expensive and are certainly not infallible. Thus, in many areas this type of work is not undertaken. Both oil and geophysical companies are spending a great deal of time and money expanding the application of geophysical surveys beyond their primary use of locating structural traps.

Finding a structural trap does not guarantee that commercial amounts of oil or gas will be found. A significant percentage of structural traps are either barren or yield only minor amounts of oil or gas; hence the importance of other factors, such as the availability of possible oil source beds and the basic reservoir characteristics of porosity and permeability. All ingredients must be present or the trap will only yield a hole in the ground and some severe disappointment. (See Figures 1-3 and 1-4 for some common types of stratigraphic and structural traps.)

## What Is an Oil or Gas Prospect?

An idea originates in the mind of an explorationist (geologist, geophysicist, landman, petroleum engineer, or entrepreneur) that in a certain area and in a rock formation, at an estimated drilling depth, there is a reasonable chance of locating a *commercial* oil or gas deposit. The proposed drill site may require a reentry, development, or wildcat well, depending on the geological or engineering concepts involved. The following paragraphs are devoted to each of these.

### Reentry Wells

*Reentry* means returning to a site where a well has been previously drilled, removing ("drilling out") the cement plugs that were set after its initial abandonment, and either performing more tests on the well or deepening it. The rationale for this operation may be that events subsequent to the first well suggest that oil or gas were inadvertently by-passed in the initial drilling or that more current knowledge of the area indicates that there are potentially productive zones below the depth to which the first well was drilled. In either instance it is frequently less costly to enter an old hole than it is to drill a new well near the same site.

Today, however, the underlying cause for most reentry operations, where deepening an old well is not the goal, is due to either an increase in oil or gas prices or an improved ability to identify a producing zone from the earlier well data.

The decision to drill a well involves an economic question. "Will the potential *profit* of this well exceed its *cost* sufficiently to warrant the *risks?*" The answer necessarily is "yes," or the well would not be drilled. When the well has reached its projected depth and has been logged and possibly tested, the next question arises "are the data in-hand encouraging enough to warrant added costs in an attempt to complete the well as an oil or gas producer?" The answer might be an unqualified "yes" or "no" or a faltering "maybe." It is the "maybe" wells of years past that are now being reentered, because present oil and gas prices tip the balance from bad to good economics and justify the risk. The reentry of old wells and development of what were once submarginal properties will continue as long as economic incentives are available to the operators.

There have been numerous instances where operators overlooked productive zones because of either a technical bias or an inability to evaluate properly the information that came from the well. All geologic provinces where oil and gas are actively sought are endowed with informal guidelines developed over many years that broadly say "where to look, what to look for, and how to evaluate." The blessing of the guidelines is that many are tried and true and, when followed, provide the technical experts some comfort and reduce the need to make hasty decisions. The disadvantage of following the guidelines lies in the perpetuation of negative factors that restrict an open mind (especially when a costly well is involved) and stifle innovation and creativity. Some real Cinderella stories can be recited about operators who should

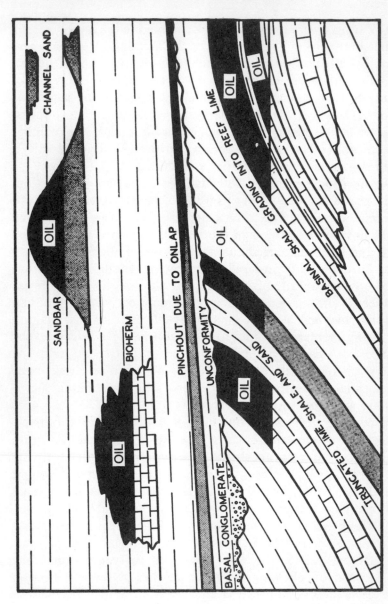

**Figure 1-3**—Common types of stratigraphic traps. (From: *Oil From Prospect to Pipeline*, 4th Ed., R.R. Wheeler and M. Whited, Gulf Pub. Co., 1981.)

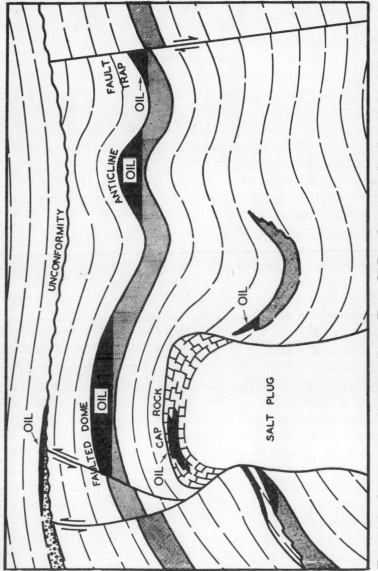

**Figure 1-4**—Common types of structural traps. (From: *Oil From Prospect to Pipeline*, 4th Ed., R.R. Wheeler and M. Whited, Gulf Pub. Co., 1981.)

not have, but did, and won. These operators could have been either naïve or creative but, in either instance, their success forced a reevaluation of existing concepts.

Not only can earlier information be viewed in a new, interpretive light, but there is also a continuing improvement in the techniques for extracting oil or gas from *tite* (tight) *formations* (rock units that lack the necessary characteristics to enable oil or gas to be easily extracted from them). Because of continued improvement in the ability to produce commercial oil or gas from many of these tite zones, there are many areas where old wells are being reentered to apply modern and frequently very costly technology.

The deepening of a pre-existing well is a matter of economics where some geological merit has been inferred for zones below those reached by the initial test, and it is less costly to take up where previous drilling ceased. A decision to deepen by reentry is either a result of new information in the region caused by recent drilling activity, or the employment of new exploration techniques in the area.

In many instances the drilling of a new well can be less costly than a reentry operation. If the old location has been abandoned for several years, then standard site preparation work, which includes preparing the *pad* (earth or gravel foundation for the drilling rig), an access road to the location, and the digging of both the *reserve pit* and the *mud pit* will have to be redone. Several cement plugs that were set during the abandonment of the initial hole will have to be "drilled out" (removed). Any "junk" (used drill bits and scrap metal) dropped in the hole when the decision to abandon the well was made, will have to be removed. Unless the abandonment was recent, most operators will elect to drill a new hole.

Deeper drilling, through either reentry or wildcat operations, in established oil or gas producing areas is a common approach in seeking new reserves. Oil and gas are known to occur in these regions and the geologic conditions that govern their entrapment are frequently amplified at greater depths. For this reason, oil or gas provinces are continuously recycled with an emphasis placed on both refined exploration techniques and the testing of successively deeper zones.

## Development Wells

A second category of well commonly encountered as an oil or gas prospect is the so-called *development* or *infield well*. These terms define a site within the producing limits of an established oil or gas field. Within the context of its definition, this type of venture is very low-risk and is thus seldom indiscriminately passed on to random investors. "Development" has a comfortable ring to it, and the word is sometimes misused in a sales talk to imply a degree of security that does not exist. Few explorationists will willingly share a true development well in a field with established economic credentials . . . except perhaps with their bank loan officers.

In some instances a region where oil or gas are commonly found, but seldom in commercial quantities, may be billed as a development area by seedy promoters. Their deals are structured in a fashion to assure a significant front-end profit (payment prior to the drilling of a well) and encumbered with an overriding royalty interest to assure some additional profit regardless of how little these marginal wells produce. Development or infield wells, when discussed in a sales talk or write-up to a would-be investor, should be viewed as a red flag. The potential investor should either run for cover or hire a consultant and then pay very careful attention to his advice.

## Step-out Wells

*Step-out* and *trend* locations describe close proximity to wells having established oil or gas merit. These sites are either in close geographic association to producing oil or gas wells or have a demonstrably inferred geological relation to the production. A step-out well is drilled along the edge of a producing area in an attempt to expand the size of a field. The term implies a low-to-moderate risk, which may or may not be warranted, based on the nature and amount of data supporting the prospect.

Trend wells are on sites that are believed to reflect geological conditions similar to neighboring oil or gas wells. The premise is that the reservoir and trap requirements necessary for a producing well can be demonstrably extended into the prospect area. Developing a good prospect on the basis of "trendology" requires a detailed analysis of all neighboring well data. The risk involved in this type of play is inversely proportional to the amount of contributing data involved in defining the trend: the more information available, the lower the risk.

## Wildcat Wells

In the oil business *wildcat* is a synonym for risk. A "wildcatter" is a "high roller," and a wildcat or exploratory well is the drilling venture that will usually result in a dry hole. But in the right area and with thorough accumulation and analysis of all data, the risk involved in this type of well can be minimal. The label is earned not by a necessary maximum risk factor, but rather by the relative isolation of the selected site to established producing wells. This separation may be geographic, where the proposed site is tens or hundreds of miles away from the nearest producing well. The separation can also be geological, where the proposed location is very close to a producing well or field, but the necessary geologic conditions for commercial oil or gas are not proven between the two points.

When an operator or promoter defines a site as a wildcat or exploratory location, he has alerted the investor to the inherent risk. The remainder of the written or verbal presentation will clarify, in varying degrees, what risk is involved. A concept will be - advanced, along with backup data, to allow the investor or his technical representative to form their own conclusions regarding the merit of the play. The investor must weigh the likelihood of success against the possibility of failure, and determine if this ratio warrants the necessary capital exposure for the estimated profit potential.

In summary, homework is desirable in school and critical in the oil business. Without research and preparation, phrases like "success" and "financial survival" will seldom pass the lips of the erstwhile oil searcher. The groundwork has to be completed before a drill site is selected. As a rule of thumb, the greater the exploration effort that goes into a drill site, the greater the likelihood of success. A drill site that has been defined only by subsurface geological work (employing data from neighboring wells), or only by geophysical techniques will have more variables than a site defined by a combination of the two approaches. Consult a specialist. Ask him if the preparatory work that went into the selection of a drill site was sufficient to define the prospect and if a reasonable likelihood of both exploratory and financial success can be anticipated.

## How Are Oil and Gas Reserve Estimates Made?

An oil and gas drilling prospectus often contains an estimate of the possible productivity of a potential well or field, and the total amount of oil or gas that can be recovered. Calculations of this sort are commonly omitted from *offering circulars* (discussed in more detail in Chapter 2), as an investor might be inadvertently misled by the numbers. The SEC is very specific in its actions regarding promoters who misinform investors.

From an explorationist's point of view, some calculations regarding oil or gas potential are necessary prior to drilling a prospect—there is no point in wasting time and money on an uneconomic venture. A common approach is to determine the volume of oil or gas believed to be present within a specific prospect and to estimate the percent of this volume that can be recovered (*recoverable reserves*) at the earth's surface. The answer, although very crude, does provide a rough guide for the economic potential of the prospect.

In determining recoverable reserves for either oil or gas it is necessary to have an estimate of how large an area will be drained by a well or a field, and what reservoir thickness is expected. In addition, an estimate will have to be made for the percent of water present (all oil and gas reservoirs contain some water), the percent of pore space (porosity) in the reservoir, and a reasonable approximation of the percent of producible oil and gas in the reservoir.

In calculations involving gas reserves several added factors are involved that result in a more complex formula than for oil. Specifically, the flow of natural gas is controlled by the pressure in the reservoir. This flow will continue until the *abandonment pressure* is reached, at which time the rate of flow is inadequate to enter into existing gas gathering systems, and the remaining gas stays in the reservoir, which is abandoned.

In reviewing any oil or gas reserve estimates it is essential that close attention be paid to the primary data. The size of the prospect should be evident on an accompanying structure contour map. The thickness of a reservoir should be consistent with neighboring wells in the area unless it is a stratigraphic play based on a thickening of a reservoir. *Isopach maps, stratigraphic cross sections,* and *well logs* are the usual base information for determining reservoir thickness. Water content and porosity estimates of the prospective zone should be substantiated by well logs from neighboring wells. Recovery factor is highly critical, and an estimate should be based on the production histories from nearby wells that either have in the past or are currently producing from the same reservoir.

Frequently, investors will become enamored with the bottom line reserve estimate and forget that these values are based on multiple assumptions. The small amount of time spent in establishing the validity of the basic data will often provide a more realistic basis for an investment decision. In rank wildcat areas this type of information should be viewed only as an educated guess.

On more than one occasion, the writer has heard an experienced oilman say, "I know my chances of finding anything are slight, but look at those reserve estimates. If I do find something, it's going to be a super giant." Not only would it be a super giant, it would be a miracle. In wildcat areas where little data are available the only restriction placed on reserve estimates is the conscience of the person performing the calculations.

# Chapter Two

# $ The Deal

The first deal was probably between a man and a woman. Whether it was a transaction centering on an apple in the Garden of Eden, or some other kind of exchange, cannot be established. Likewise, the first oil deal has been totally obscured by time. Some speculation concerns a wily rug merchant who convinced an early Pharaoh that his preservation could be assured by the application of pitch to his "windings."

Oil has been bartered for several thousands of years. It has been employed not only for the preservation of mummies but also as a sealant on early sailing vessels and, in some instances, as a medication.

Growth of the petroleum industry since the Drake well in Pennsylvania in 1859 has followed the pattern of demand and supply, with levels of exploration and discovery broadly keeping pace with consumption. Only in recent years has oil demand outstripped discovery and led to a public awareness of the true meaning of the term "depletable commodity." Oil is the springboard that catapulted the United States to the forefront in transportation and industry. The rate of descent will hinge largely on the continued development of petroleum reserves until an effective alternate energy source is established.

Oil and gas are found by drilling, and most drilling is the end result of satisfactory deals between parties interested in taking a reasonable, shared profit. A measured appraisal of all ingredients in the transaction is the formula for long-term success.

In the early days of the domestic oil business boom towns arose at the sites of new discoveries, and leases offsetting wells were frequently sold or traded on a daily basis. Fortunes were made and lost, and leasebrokers and wildcatters with good instincts prospered. The boom towns are gone, but the custom of dealing in leases and drilling ventures is ingrained in the oil seeker.

## What Is an Oil Deal?

"An 'oil deal' is an agreement between two or more parties whereby one party agrees to sell, transfer, or trade an interest in a drilling venture in return for money, negotiable securities, furs, jewelry, chickens, etc. . . . The deal may be concluded with a handshake, a lengthy contract, or gunfire. Regardless of the closing ceremonies, a deal is a deal and involved parties are expected (demanded) to fulfill their part of the agreement."

An oil deal in the usual sense is the offering by one party of an opportunity to a second party to participate in both the purchase of oil and gas leases and in the drilling of one or several wells. The agreement may be more comprehensive and include the development of an entire program where geological and geophysical studies are conducted and where additional leases may be obtained.

Most organizations that involve themselves with small investors provide a summary of their program in an *offering circular*. Federal regulations require that this document be prepared and distributed to the investors in this type of program and that certain cautionary statements and information be included in the circular.

Specifically, the investor's financial liability and his earned interest in the venture must be presented. Basically, the cost and profit potential to the participant are the main ingredients to be reviewed in this type of summary. Geological merit of the prospect may shape a decision for individual investors but will not alter the stated terms of the agreement that the ultimate participants will abide by.

Here is a sample deal, taken from an offering circular:

> For the sum of $17,500, we agree to assign to you 5% of the gross production, this being 7.5% of the Working Interest mentioned above, and to drill, test, and complete a well to be named _____ at no further cost to you, other than your proportionate share of any and all operating expenses accrued in the production of oil and/or gas from this well, to a depth sufficient to test the _____ sand at approximately 5000 feet. Should this well be abandoned as a "dry hole," we agree to refund $7500 to you, and the well shall be considered complete and plugged.

The basic deal, although awkwardly put, is that an investor will pay $17,500 for a 7.5% working interest in the well. The total cost of the program, which includes unspecified charges and one well, is therefore $233,333.33 ($17,500 divided by 0.075). It is also stated that the investor will be assigned 5% of the gross production. This means that the deal is being offered with a net revenue interest of 66.6667% (5% divided by 7.5%). In other words, if an investor pays 100% of costs, he earns 66.6667% of any profits.

It is then pointed out that if this well is a dry hole the investor will be refunded $7500. Now, the full financial deal can be viewed. (See Tables 2-1 and 2-2.)

Whether this deal is good or bad is up to the investor. In the writer's opinion the greater the degree of difficulty in extracting the essential information from the offering circular, the shakier the deal. The offerer of a deal knows when the terms are good and will thus repeatedly emphasize this positive factor rather than hide it in the foliage.

In any negotiations involving an oil deal, ask these questions:

1. What percentage working interest in the program is being obtained by the payment of the required money?

2.  What net revenue interest is applied to this working interest?

3.  Is the net revenue interest the same both before and after payout? If not, then how do they differ?

Frequently, the phrase "standard oilfield deal" will be employed in opening the bargaining ceremonies. If this format is agreed upon, the buyer is willing to pay one-third of all costs to casing point and one-fourth of all completion costs. In return the investor will earn one-fourth of the revenues assigned to the working interest participants. In other words, if the buyer agrees to pay 100% of the costs, he will earn 75% of the profits, exclusive of any royalty and overriding royalties incorporated in the deal. As an example, assume that an investor has taken a 10% working interest in a deal, on a one-third for one-quarter basis, and that

### Table 2-1
### If the Well Is Successful

|          | Amount paid   | Revenue earned (%) |
|----------|---------------|--------------------|
| Lessor   | 0             | 33.3333            |
| Promoter | 0             |                    |
| Investors| $233,333.33   | 66.6667            |

### Table 2-2
### If the Well Is Plugged and Abandoned Without Testing

|          | Amount paid    |
|----------|----------------|
| Lessor   | 0              |
| Promoter | 0              |
| Investors| $133,333.33    |

there is a 12.5% landowner royalty and a 12.5% overriding royalty interest to the promoter. The investor pays 10% of all costs, which is his working interest. To calculate his revenue interest, it is necessary to reduce the 100% revenue that is available by the agreed upon burdens (i.e., the landowner's royalty and the promoter's overriding royalty interest). This calculation leaves a total revenue interest of 75% in the deal. What percent does the investor earn?

Actually, the solution is fairly straightforward: simply multiply 0.75 by the net revenue interest available in the deal by the percent working interest held by the investor.

Thus 0.75 x 75% x 0.1 = 5.625%, which is the percent of revenues that will be earned by paying a 10% working interest.

In the oil business "a talented geologist may be called an oil finder, but a good businessman is called a millionaire." A good geologist can be a good businessman, but commonly their drummers are tapping out a different cadence. The giants of the business are those who know their economics, and who surround themselves with salaried experts. Their approach is first to determine if a deal is good or bad and, if good, to concern themselves with its technical merit. No matter how geologically attractive a deal might be, if the economics won't stand up, it's a bad deal.

It is strongly advised that any investor in an oil or gas deal have an expert review the numbers. If these are satisfactory, then have a judgment rendered on the technical merit of the venture.

## How Is an Oil Deal Evaluated?

"The basic evaluation of any oil deal relies heavily on a careful analysis of the *crap* factor. This widely used acronym refers to a *cost, risk,* and *profit* analysis."

The three components of any oil deal are lease position, geological attractiveness, and economics. Lease position refers to the size of the area on which oil and gas leases have been obtained, and how these leases are distributed with regard to the drilling prospect or prospects.

## Lease Position

The initial purchase of the leases is handled by a *petroleum landman* or lease broker who negotiates with the owner of mineral interests (usually the landowner) for the right to explore and drill for oil or gas on his property. The normal points which are haggled over are the lease bonus, the lease term, the annual rental, lessor royalty, work obligations, and the weather. Extraneous provisions are occasionally inserted in some leases and result in premature aging of oil company lease clerks.

In acquiring leases a cash bonus is normally paid on a per-acre basis. The bonus can vary from a "free lease" or nothing per acre to many hundreds or thousands of dollars per acre. In general, the greater the geological attractiveness of an area, the greater the competition to obtain leases, usually with a corresponding escalation in lease bonus costs. Leases can still be obtained in many areas that have excellent oil or gas potential for as little as $15 per acre. Beauty is in the eyes of the beholder, and thus there are areas where oil has never been nor likely ever will be found, but where the lessor still expects an extravagant lease bonus.

Once a lease is obtained, the oil and gas rights therein are for a specified period of time (usually one, three, five, or ten years) and require an annual rental on a per-acre basis. If oil or gas production is obtained on the lease, the mineral rights, either on a portion or on the entire lease, will normally be retained by the lessee for the duration of production. In Texas, a dollar per acre is a common annual rental, in some other states it is substantially higher. In south Louisiana, for example, the annual delay rental often equals the lease bonus.

Lessor (landowner) royalty is the key to most leases, as this percentage of gross proceeds retained by the lessor determines the viability and marketability of many oil deals. Custom dictates that 12.5% is the minimum royalty a lessor will receive. This 12.5% royalty, commonly referred to as *one-eighth,* means that for every dollar's worth of oil or gas produced from a lessor's property, he is entitled to 12.5 cents. The only exception to this royalty is if the lessor only owns a portion of the area from which a well is producing (production unit), and in that situation he is entitled to a *pro rata* share of the royalty.

While the minimum lessor royalty is 12.5%, it can increase significantly from that point. Any amount above the 12.5% figure is called *excess royalty.* Normal values of royalty above the one-eighth (12.5%) level are: five-thirty seconds (15.625%), one-sixth (16.6667%), three-sixteenths (18.75%), one-fifth (20.0%), and one-quarter (25.00%). Any royalty above the one-eighth is normally negotiated (hotly contested) by the landman and only awarded in areas that have a higher than usual geologic merit.

A provision may be inserted in the lease whereby the lessee (the party who purchases the lease) is required to have a well drilled on the property within a specified period of time. This provision may be included with a continuous drilling obligation to require that a new well be periodically initiated within specific time intervals (three months, six months, one year).

The list of provisions and clauses that can be inserted in a lease is virtually endless. The lessor and lessee are each trying to protect their interest from the oil company landman, who simply wishes to keep his skin and job intact.

## Geological Attractiveness

The geological attractiveness of an area has been broadly and, in some instances, most precisely determined prior to the purchase of the leases. If the area was not studied in great detail before the leases were obtained, then it certainly will be before any wells are drilled. Normally, a subsurface study is conducted whereby information from other wells in the area is collected and reviewed. This study permits the geologist to make some predictions regarding the likelihood of oil or gas at specific sites within the leased area. Maps will be constructed that will indicate the rationale for drilling and will show the location of the preferred site or sites, along with the necessary depths to drill.

Geophysical and especially seismic work may be undertaken, which considerably increases the cost of the exploration program but which frequently provides the margin between success and failure. In many small-investor deals seismic results are not included, generally because of the high costs of such surveys, but also because many of these investment programs are located in areas where seismic surveys are not a satisfactory tool.

The risk factor normally associated with the oil business is based on the relatively low success percentage of exploratory wildcat wells (wells that are both geologically and geographically separated from commercial oil or gas wells, past or present). This basis is primarily a geological factor (discounting the mechanical risk involved in drilling a well) which can be reduced but not eliminated. To minimize this risk, the explorationist must completely familiarize himself with the geological conditions that must be met within a particular region to provide for a commercial accumulation of oil or gas. He then must be prepared to employ the necessary tools to determine if such conditions are present and, if so, then at what specific sites. At this stage, his work done, he has followed a formula which through repeated use will establish his credentials as an oil finder.

Regardless of his efforts, a significant percentage of his wells will be dry (nonproductive). This results from what appears to be the capricious behavior of oil and gas, and the inability of mortals, even with sophisticated instrumentation, to predict completely the character of rock bodies that are situated thousands of feet beneath the earth's surface. The risk is real; it can be reduced but not eliminated.

## Economics

In evaluating the business portion of an oil and gas deal the investor should make some estimate of the profit potential for the promoter, regardless of the outcome of a well or wells. Will he, in fact, make a substantial profit even on a dry hole? Profit is obviously the motive for the promoter in assembling the deal, and for the investor in buying a deal. The seller requires some profit, regardless of the outcome of the well, to continue in business. On the other hand, a deal without potential profit to the investor is unsaleable.

There are three primary areas where the originator of a drilling venture can be assigned of some financial benefits regardless of whether or not he finds oil or gas. A common profit center in many programs involves *lease acquisition costs*. It is not uncommon for a lessee (seller) to obtain acreage at $5 to $25 per acre and to incorporate it in a deal with a $50 to $150 per-acre price tag. A recent review of a program in Oklahoma indicated a $10,000 lease cost for an 80-acre tract of land. A landman familiar with this area estimated that lease cost in this relatively inactive area should vary from $10 to $25 per acre. This provided an apparent gain of $8000 to $9200, from which some broker fees, geological costs, and overhead expenses had to be deducted.

While it is both legal and widely accepted to promote land costs, an investor should review the per-acre fee for which he is billed. No guidelines can be laid down to differentiate between a reasonable promotion and an onerous load. If lease costs exceed $100 per acre, and the investor is concerned about an overpromotion, he should seek the services of a consultant landman familiar with the prospect area.

A second potential profit center for the promoter lies in a general category which includes legal fees, management fees, and costs of offering. In some instances the items are tabulated with specific costs assigned to each; other times a percentage of the program subscription will cover this category. In reviewing a program in Oklahoma the total legal and printing costs were shown as $7000, with overhead costs set in the operating agreement at $1500 per month for a well while drilling and $150 per month for each producing well. Any profit derived from these amounts would be inconsequential.

A separate organization with its operations in Texas charges a percentage of its total subscriptions for leases, overhead, offering costs, and legal and management fees. The total subscription amount was projected to be between $350,000 and $525,000 with 8.5% ($29,750-$44,625) set aside to cover these costs. Lease costs are not stated in the offering circular, and thus a judgment cannot be rendered on these figures. For each successful well in this program, the operator will receive $300 per month per well for operating charges. This fee is reasonable for operating charges on a per producing well basis. The monthly per-well costs for both drilling and producing wells is necessarily spelled out in an operating agreement with its attached accounting procedure which governs the association between the promoter and the investor.

One fraudulent deal reviewed several years ago not only garnered a heavy profit on both lease costs and turnkey (i.e., a fixed price established for the performance of specific work) drilling operations but also levied a staggering management and operations fee. Management and operations fees are the most difficult to evaluate from a profit point of view. This situation results because many cost items are often grouped together, and because many offering circulars are purposefully vague about these costs.

Turnkey drilling and turnkey completion costs are desirable from the investor's point of view, as they precisely define the amount of money required to participate in a well or wells. The distinction between drilling and completion operations is made following the open hole logging of a well. (See page 59.) All operations prior to and including open hole logging are considered part of the drilling costs, that is, the well costs to casing point. After reviewing the open hole logs, a decision is made either to plug and abandon the well or to attempt a completion. If the decision is reached to complete the well, then subsequent charges are referred to as completion costs. These costs normally involve the setting of production casing, cementing the casing, cased hole logging, perforating, acidizing, and possibly fracturing. If the well is successful, then wellhead equipment, storage tanks, a separator, and possibly a pump will be required at the surface. Completion costs and production facilities can be quite expensive.

Drilling contractors normally charge either a footage rate (a set cost per foot drilled), or a day rate (a set cost for each 24 hours of drilling) when drilling a well. For a turnkey job (a fixed price to drill a well to the required depth) to casing point, the contractor will normally quote a figure to the operator with added charges to account for unexpected developments. The operator then in turn may incorporate other charges in this price to pass onto the investor. If the operator employs his own drilling unit in the program, his profit potential could be twofold. An operator is frequently called to render judgment on the appropriateness of some costs relating to drilling procedures. If he also controls the drilling company, his judgment may be clouded. Consequently, it is advisable that investors in drilling programs try to avoid situations where the drilling and production operations are both controlled by the same entity.

## Net Revenue Interest

For the professional investor in oil and gas deals, the key economic figure is the *net revenue interest* (percent of profits earned by investor) that is earned by a specific working interest (percent of program costs paid by investor). Any drilling and/or completion operation necessarily must be funded for 100% of the cost. If an individual pays 10% of the costs, then that person has a 10% working interest in the venture. This calculation is straightforward, and an investor generally has a clear picture of his financial liability in a drilling program. Less clear is the net revenue, as this calculation is frequently obscured by excess royalty, overriding royalty, and back-in after payout.

When a lease is obtained, then the lessor retains a royalty, commonly one-eighth (12.5%). Assuming that leases have been obtained for a 12.5% royalty, the working interest participants at that stage can earn at a maximum only 87.5% of any oil and gas revenues from the lease.

## Table 2-3
### Working Interest and Revenue Interest Comparison

|  | Working Interest Amount Spent (%) | Revenue Interest Amount Earned (%) |
|---|---|---|
| Lessor | 0 | 12.5 |
| Geologist | 0 | 2.0 |
| Promoter | 0 | 5.5 |
| Investor | 100 | 80.0 |
|  | 100 | 100.0 |

The geologist involved in the program may have agreed to perform his study for a 2% overriding royalty interest (ORRI). This agreement means that the geologist will receive 2% and the lessor will receive 12.5% of all oil and gas revenues without spending any of their own money in the program. The promoter may elect to retain an overriding royalty interest and, as an example, let this figure equal 5.5%. A comparison of working interest and revenue interest at this stage appears in Table 2-3.

Thus, in the previous example, an individual with a 10% working interest in a drilling venture will have an 8% revenue interest. In other words, for every $10,000 the program earns, he will receive $800.

In addition to the overriding royalty interest held by the promoter, there is sometimes a *back-in working interest* after payout. This clause simply means that after the working-interest participants have recovered all their costs from a successful producing well, the point of payout has been reached, and a back-in will take effect. The participants with the back-in then pay their share of all costs from the time of payout and receive their proportionate share of subsequent revenues.

Employing the same example, but inserting a conversion of the promoter's 5.5% overriding royalty to a 25% back-in working interest, the various interests are shown in Table 2-4.

### Table 2-4
### Working Interest and Revenue Interest Comparison
### with Promoter's Back-in Working Interest

|  | Working Interest | | Revenue Interest | |
|  | Before Payout(%) | After Payout(%) | Before Payout(%) | After Payout(%) |
|---|---|---|---|---|
| Lessor | 0 | 0 | 12.5 | 12.5 |
| Geologist | 0 | 0 | 2.0 | 2.0 |
| Promoter | 0 | 25 | 5.5 | 21.375 |
| Investors | 100 | 75 | 80.0 | 64.125 |
|  | 100 | 100 | 100.0 | 100.0 |

Note: The after-payout revenue interest for the promoter was obtained by
multiplying 25% x 85.5%. The 85.5% figure was derived by subtracting
the lessor and geologist royalty from 100%.

Small-investor deals (less than $10,000 investment per person) usually provide a circular which includes all information concerning working interest and revenue interest, although the data frequently require careful reading and some calculations.

### Example 1

Promoter is carried 10% (the investor is paying for these costs) to casing point and pays 10% of completion costs. After payout, the promoter receives an additional 10% revenue interest. The lease description in the offering circular points out that a 100% working interest earns a 72% net revenue interest. This description means that in addition to the lessor royalty there are overriding royalty interests assigned to unnamed parties. (See Table 2-5.)

### Example 2

Leases were obtained by the promoter for a one-eighth royalty (12.5%). Production revenues will be distributed 85% to the investors and 15% to the promoter until payout. After payout, the investors will receive 70% of the revenues, the promoter will receive 28% of the revenues, and the geologist will receive 2% of the revenues. In addition, a 5% ORRI is assigned to another party following payout. (See Table 2-6.)

### Table 2-5
### Small-Investor Deal—Example 1

| | Working Interest | | Revenue Interest | |
|---|---|---|---|---|
| | Before Casing(%) | After Casing(%) | Before Casing(%) | After Casing(%) |
| Lessor | 0 | 0 | 12.5 | 12.5 |
| Geologist | 0 | 0 | 2.0 | 2.0 |
| Unnamed ORRI | 0 | 0 | 13.5 | 13.5 |
| Promoter | 0 | 10 | 7.2 | 14.4 |
| Investors | 100 | 90 | 64.8 | 57.6 |
| | 100 | 100 | 100 | 100 |

### Table 2-6
### Small-Investor Deal—Example 2

| | Working Interest | | Revenue Interest | |
|---|---|---|---|---|
| | Before Payout(%) | After Payout(%) | Before Payout(%) | After Payout(%) |
| Lessor | 0 | 0 | 12.50 | 12.50 |
| Geologist | 0 | 0 | 0 | 1.65 |
| Promoter | 0 | 0 | 13.125 | 23.10 |
| Unnamed ORRI | 0 | 0 | 0 | 5.00 |
| Investors | 100 | 100 | 74.375 | 57.75 |
| | 100 | 100 | 100.0 | 100.0 |

There is a vagueness to the previous statements because of the intermixing of percentages for two separate items. After the first statement (in which the one-eighth royalty is dispensed with), the remaining percentages are referring to fractional amounts of 87.5% rather than 100%. The last statement concerning the 5% ORRI refers back to the initial 100%.

The preceding calculations are straightforward and could have been inserted in the initial sales brochure. It can only be assumed that the promoter felt that the advertisement of the low net revenue interest after payout would jeopardize his sales program. In a stepwise fashion the calculations for revenue interest proceed as follows:

*Before Payout*

85% of revenue to investors:    85% x 87.5% = 74.375%
15% of revenue to promoter:    15% x 87.5% = 13.125%

*After Payout*

5% unnamed ORRI reduces 87.5% to 82.5%
2% of revenue to geologist—2% of 82.5%    =   1.65%
28% of revenue to promoter—28% of 82.5% = 23.10%
70% of revenue to investors—70% of 82.5%  = 57.75%
                                                              82.5%

To a sophisticated investor, the bottom line is revenue interest before and after payout. Specific questions concerning these amounts should be directed to the promoter prior to consumating a deal. In both examples cited the load is heavy and could only be justified by exceptionally attractive prospects. The phrase "standard oilfield deal" is frequently employed in these negotiations.

Assuming a lease was obtained for a one-eighth royalty (12.5%), the revenue interest is 87.5% for a 100% working interest.

If a group of investors acquire the deal on a one-third for one-quarter basis, the breakdown of interest is as in Table 2-7. If the

### Table 2-7
### One-Third for One-Quarter Interest

|  | Working Interest | | Revenue Interest(%) |
|---|---|---|---|
|  | Before Casing Point(%) | After Casing Point (%) | |
| Lessor | 0 | 0 | 12.5 |
| Promoter | 0 | 25 | 21.875 |
| Investors | 100 | 75 | 65.625 |
|  | 100 | 100 | 100.00 |

lessor royalty had been 25% rather than 12.5%, then figures are altered as in Table 2-8.

In determining the before and after payout revenue interest in any deal, attention should first be focused on the lessor's royalty and on any overriding royalty interest involved. These two percentages are inviolate and should be deducted immediately from the 100% revenue interest that is available with any producing property. The percentage revenue that remains is then divided between the promoter and the investors along whatever lines have been agreed upon. This calculation determines the revenue interest to the investor before payout. If an ORRI is attached after payout, this sum is added to the lessor's royalty and any other overriding royalty interests. This sum is then deducted

### Table 2-8
### Lessor Royalty at 25%

|  | Working Interest | | Revenue Interest(%) |
|---|---|---|---|
|  | Before Casing Point(%) | After Casing Point(%) | |
| Lessor | 0 | 0 | 25.0 |
| Promoter | 0 | 25 | 18.75 |
| Investors | 100 | 75 | 56.25 |
|  | 100 | 100 | 100.0 |

from 100% to determine the percent to be split after payout between the promoter and investors as outlined in the original agreement.

A back-in interest can be directed to either the working interest or the revenue interest. If it is a back-in working interest, its corresponding revenue interest is obtained by multiplying the back-in percent by the initial revenue interest (100% less lessor royalty and ORRI). The revenue interest earned by the investor is then reduced by a corresponding amount.

If the back-in interest is based on revenue interest, this percent is simply added to the lessor royalty and the ORRI and subtracted from 100% with the remaining revenue interest earned by the investor after payout.

The sole purpose for any investor to participate in an oil deal is profit. He is required to accept most technical data on faith or to employ a specialist who can evaluate the potential of a program. Routinely, he should closely analyze all cost items and make estimates as to whether promoter profits on leases, drilling, and overhead are reasonable or excessive. A close evaluation should be made on working interest percentage and net revenue interest, both before and after payout. If these varying interests are not clearly spelled out in the offering circular, then he should recognize that the cloudiness or vagueness is likely an attempt to obscure the facts of a "tough" or poor deal.

## How Does an Investor Get in an Oil Deal?

If an investor prefers to tie up funds and be a disinterested spectator in the oil business, then the stock market is his best approach. After the initial decision to invest, he is then confronted with the problem of deciding the type of organization that best suits his interests. One approach is to simply buy stock in a major oil corporation, sit back, and let economic or political factors determine whether he wins or loses. The investor's role, aside from his initial capital expenditure, is to review the various Exchange activities and agonize over daily variations in the stock's value. This approach is the most conservative and, for oil and gas investors, sometimes the most rewarding.

Extending downward from the major oil corporations are a wide variety of lesser-size organizations where the main emphasis is in the search and the development of oil and gas reserves. Stock can be purchased in most of these organizations where the impact of an "exciting new discovery" has a more tangible effect for the stockholders than a similar situation with the "majors." Shareholders receive notifications of a company's success or failures by means of information circulars that contain dreary recitations of assets and liabilities. There is obviously a remoteness to this type of organization that many investors dislike. It is still too large for personal contact to be made.

Many investors prefer a higher-risk investment that provides a greater potential of both personal involvement and profits. Their hole card is that the funds they are risking are largely destined for Uncle Sam's coffers. In their judgment the high risk that they are accepting is compensated by the tax advantages they will receive—win, lose, or draw.

An investor who elects to participate in a single well or in a venture comprising a number of wells is unquestionably assuming the maximum oil investment risk. This risk is a highly specific program in a field where the best chances for survival lie in diversification. Statistically, it can be demonstrated that the larger the number of wells in a program (and each well shares the same risk of failure), the greater the likelihood that one or more will be successful.

As an example, if a drilling program takes place in a region where the commercial success of exploratory wells is 15%, Table 2-9 can be constructed.

The chart indicates the likelihood of one oil or gas discovery in a two-well program is only 25.5% but increases to 39.93% in a six-well program. A calculation like this one simply provides the statistical risk involved in drilling in an area with a known percentage of success. The greater the number of wells drilled in the region, the greater the likelihood of one or more successes.

Success stories abound in the oil business, and listeners are quick to zero in on organizations that are reported to have more than a normal share of good fortune. The final yardstick in

## Table 2-9
## Drilling Risk Chart

| Probable Successes | 15% Success Number of Wells Drilled | | | | |
|---|---|---|---|---|---|
| | **2** | **3** | **4** | **5** | **6** |
| 0 | 72.25% | 61.41% | 52.20% | 44.37% | 39.93% |
| 1 | 25.50% | 32.51% | 36.85% | 39.15% | 37.71% |
| 2 | 2.25% | 5.74% | 9.75% | 13.82% | 17.62% |
| 3 | | 0.34% | 1.15% | 2.44% | 4.14% |
| 4 | | | 0.05% | 0.21% | 0.55% |
| 5 | | | | 0.01% | 0.04% |
| 6 | | | | | nil |

evaluating a company's success is its profit column based on oil or gas revenue. Estimates of recoverable reserves in the ground should not be accepted as fact, as the path from reservoir to pipeline is bounded by disappointments and surprises.

There is a select group of citizens sought out by many oil companies as potential investors. The credentials to join this group are a minimum annual income on the order of $50,000-$100,000, and an acute awareness of the tax problems associated with a high salary. Specific fields that are commonly approached by promoters include entertainment, sports, legal, medical, and dental. It is impossible for vendors of deals to contact everyone, and thus there is a concentration on specific professions that have established income credentials. If you are interested, and fall into any of the previous categories, stay close to the telephone.

# Chapter Three

# $ The Turf

In the search for oil or gas no one factor is of greater importance than another. A good geological prospect is essential, or oil probably will not be found. A good deal with fair terms is critical, or a profit will not be made, and the drilling incentive will not exist. An oil and gas lease is required, as both the oil prospect and the profit potential are meaningless without one. Oil and gas leases are fundamental to the business.

## What Is an Oil and Gas Lease?

An oil and gas lease is a legal document in which the holder of the mineral interests on a specified tract of land grants an individual or company the right to enter the property and to conduct a search for oil and gas. The search may involve surface geological studies, soil analysis, geophysical exploration, and drilling operations. If oil or gas is found, then the lessee (organization or individual who acquires the lease) has the right to install any equipment on the premises that is necessary for the production, storage, sale, and transportation of the product. Conditions are sometimes inserted in a standard oil and gas lease form that will abridge the customarily accepted rights of the lessee.

41

# OIL AND GAS LEASE

### WITH POOLING AND REGULATION CLAUSES

**This Agreement,** Made and entered into this _____ day of _____, 19___

by and between _____

of _____ hereinafter called lessor (whether one or more), and

_____ hereinafter called lessee.

**Witnesseth,** That the said lessor, for and in consideration of _____

_____ DOLLARS cash in hand paid, receipt of which is hereby acknowledged, and of the covenants and agreements hereinafter contained on the part of lessee, to be paid, kept and performed, has granted, demised, leased and let and by these presents does grant, demise, lease and let unto the said lessee, for the sole and only purpose of mining and operating for oil and gas, and laying pipe lines, power stations and structures thereon to produce, save and take care of said products, all that certain tract of land situate in the County of _____

State of _____, described as follows, to-wit:

of Section _____ Township _____ Range _____ and containing _____ acres, more or less.

It is agreed that this lease shall remain in force for a term of _____ years from this date, and as long thereafter as oil or gas, or either of them, is produced from said lands by the lessee.

In consideration of the premises the said lessee covenants and agrees:

To deliver to the credit of lessor, free of cost, in the pipe lines or tanks to which he may connect his wells, the equal one-eighth part of all oil produced and saved from said leased premises.

And where gas only is found, one-eighth of the value of all raw gas at the mouth of the well, while said gas is being used or sold off the premises, payment for gas so used or sold to be made monthly. The lessor to have gas free of cost from any gas well on said premises for all stoves and all inside lights in the principal dwelling house on said land by making _____ own connections with the well at _____ own risk and expense.

To pay lessor for gas produced from any oil well and used off the premises one-eighth of the value of the raw gas at the mouth of the well, payment for the gas so used or sold to be made quarterly.

If no well be commenced on said land on or before the _____ day of _____, 19___ the lease shall terminate as to both parties, unless the lessee on or before that date shall pay or tender to the lessor, or to the lessor's credit in the _____ Bank at _____ or its successors, which shall continue as the depository regardless of changes in the ownership of said land, the sum of _____

DOLLARS, which shall operate as a rental

and cover the privilege of deferring the commencement of a well for _____ months from said date. In like manner and upon like payments or tenders the commencement of a well may be further deferred for like period of the same number of months successively. And it is understood and agreed that the consideration first recited herein, the down payment, ... covers not only the privileges granted to the date when first rental is payable as aforesaid, but also the lessee's option of extending th... period as aforesaid, and any and all other rights conferred.

Lessee, at its option, is hereby given the right and power to pool or combine the ... covered by this lease or any portion thereof, with other land, lease or leases in the immediate vicinity thereof, when in lessee's judgment it is necessary or advisable to do so in order to properly develop and operate said lease premises so as to promote the conservation of oil, gas or other minerals in and under and that may be produced from said premises, such pooling to be of tracts contiguous to one another and to be into a unit or units and under and not exceeding 40 acres each in the event of an oil well, or into a unit or units or into a unit or units in the event of a gas well. Lessee shall execute in writing and record in the conveyance records of the county in which the land herein leased is situated an instrument identifying and describing the pooled acreage. The entire acreage so pooled into a tract or unit shall be treated, for all purposes except the payment of royalties on production from the pooled unit, as if it were included in this lease. If production is found on the pooled acreage, it shall be treated as if production is had from this lease, whether the well or wells be located on the premises covered by this lease or not. In lieu of the royalties elsewhere herein specified, lessor shall receive on production from a unit so pooled only such portion of the royalty stipulated herein as the amount of his acreage placed in the unit or his royalty interest therein on an acreage basis, bears to the total acreage so pooled into the particular unit involved.

Should the first well drilled on the above described land be a dry hole, then, and in that event, if a second well is not commenced on said land within twelve months from the expiration of the last rental period which rental has been paid this lease shall terminate as to both parties, unless the lessee on or before the expiration of said twelve months shall resume the payment of rentals in the same amount and in the same manner as hereinbefore provided. And it is agreed that upon the resumption of the payment of rentals, as above provided, that the last preceding paragraph hereof, governing the payment of rentals and the effect thereof, shall continue in force just as though there had been no interruption in the rental payments.

If said lessor owns a less interest in the above described land than the entire and undivided fee simple estate therein, then the royalties and rentals herein provided shall be paid the lessor only in the proportion which his interest bears to the whole and all undivided fee.

Lessee shall have the right to use, free of cost, gas, oil and water produced on said land for its operations thereon, except water from the wells of lessor.

When requested by lessor, lessee shall bury its pipe lines below plow depth.

No well shall be drilled nearer than 200 feet to the house or barn now on said premises, without the written consent of the lessor.

Lessee shall pay for damages caused by its operation to growing crops on said land.

Lessee shall have the right at any time to remove all machinery and fixtures placed on said premises, including the right to draw and remove casing.

If the estate of either party hereto is assigned, and the privileges of assigning in whole or part is expressly allowed—the covenants hereof shall extend to their heirs, executors, administrators, successors or assigns, but no change in the ownership of the land or assignment of rentals or royalties shall be binding on the lessee until after the lessee has been furnished with a written transfer or assignment or a true copy thereof; and it is hereby agreed that in the event this lease shall be assigned as to a part or as to parts of the above described lands and the assignee or assignees of such part or parts shall fail or make default in the payment of the proportionate part of the rents due from him or them, such default shall not operate to defeat or affect this lease in so far as it covers a part or parts of said lands upon which the said lessee or any assignee hereof shall make due payment of said rental.

Lessor hereby warrants and agrees to defend the title to the lands herein described, and agrees that the lessee shall have the right at ... time to redeem for lessor, by payment, any mortgages, taxes or other liens on the above described lands, in the event of default of payment by lessor, and be subrogated to the rights of the holder thereof.

All express or implied covenants of this lease shall be subject to all Federal and State Laws, Executive Orders, Rules or Regulations, and this lease shall not be terminated, in whole or in part, nor lessee held liable in damages, for failure to comply therewith, if compliance is prevented by, or if such failure is the result of any such Law, Order, Rule or Regulation.

In Testimony Whereof We Sign, this the _____ day of _____ 19__

_____ (SEAL)

Witness

Figure 3-1—Standard lease document. (From: *Oil From Prospect to Pipeline*, 4th Ed., R.R. Wheeler and M. Whited, Gulf Pub. Co., 1981.)

When a lease has been obtained, the lessee wll pay a small fee and have the document recorded at the appropriate county clerk's office. An official record of the lease date is essential in the event the lessor has inadvertently leased his property to other parties. In some states a legal judgment in a conflicting lease ownership suit is more influenced by the date the documents were officially recorded than by the date they were signed or when a bonus was paid. Such states are called "race-to-the-courthouse states."

In return for granting these rights the lessor (owner of the mineral interests on the property) will receive a royalty on all oil or gas produced in association with the lease and usually some bonus consideration with a per-acre dollar value. In addition, the lessor will be compensated for all land/crop damages inflicted on his property as a consequence of any exploration and drilling activity. If the lease covers a time interval in excess of one year, the lessor is commonly entitled to an annual rental on a per-acre basis, as spelled out in the lease.

The text of a standard lease form is precisely worded to define the benefits and obligations of both the lessee and the lessor. Provisions are frequently added to a lease with their significance ranging from picayunish to monumental. Once a lease has been signed by the necessary party or parties, the terms as outlined therein are legally binding, and all parties are required to fulfill their part of any stated obligations.

When a lease has been obtained and duly recorded, the lessee, unless restricted by specific provisions, can either initiate his own program or sell, transfer, or trade the lease. If the lease term is short (one year or less), the actions of the lessee will be characterized either by an accelerated work program or a deal where the lease is dispensed with. Figure 3-1 is one form of a standard oil and gas lease.

A *farmout* is a common approach for obtaining an oil and gas lease or leases from the existing lessee. In this transaction the party desiring the lease will approach the lessee with some offer of work (a seismic or drilling program) to earn a portion of the oil and gas rights under consideration. He may request that the acreage be "checkerboarded," where each party retains the oil and gas rights on alternate parcels of land. The size of each checkerboard might be 10, 20, 40, or 80 acres on an oil prospect, or 160, 320, or 640 acres on a gas prospect. The advantage of a checkerboard arrangement to the lease holder is that he has the opportunity of viewing the results of one or more wells before he undertakes the drilling of his own acreage. If the holder of the farmout is unsuccessful in his drilling efforts, the original lease holder will have thus saved himself the necessary drilling costs that would have been required to test the acreage. A checkerboard pattern for farmout acreage is not as popular now as it was in the past.

More commonly, a farmout involves an entire block of land, usually comprising several or many different leases. The interested party will approach the lease holder and request a farmout based on some proposed work program and will offer him some retained interest in oil or gas produced from the property. If the lease holder is willing to farmout the acreage, the retained interest (usually a royalty or back-in working interest or both) and the proposed work program become the main topics of negotiation. A cash consideration will not enter the discussion, as the repayment of lease costs removes the deal from the farmout category.

When the terms of a farmout have been settled, a *farmout agreement* is drawn up with the involved parties or their representatives acknowledging the document. In addition to the terms set forth in the farmout agreement, the "farmin" party will also be required to adhere to all terms and conditions as provided in each separate lease that relates to the property, and as originally agreed on by the lessee. The stated work program will then begin along the prescribed schedule, and all documents relating to the transaction will be duly recorded at the appropriate county clerk's office. Figure 3-2 is a farmout agreement.

AAPL FORM 635

# FARMOUT AGREEMENT

DATE:

TO:                                    RE:

In consideration of the benefits to accrue to the parties hereto and the covenants and obligations to be kept by you, it is hereby mutually agreed as follows:

## I  ACREAGE:

We represent without Warranty of Title of any kind or character that we hold Oil and Gas Leases or Mineral Interests described as follows:

We agree to deliver to you such abstracts and other title papers as we have in our files at this time, and at your sole cost, risk and expense you agree to conduct such Title Examinations and secure such curative matter as is necessary to satisfy yourselves that Title is acceptable to you.

## II  OBLIGATIONS:

(A) TEST WELL:  On or before the____day of_____, 19____, you agree to commence, or cause to be commenced the actual drilling of a well for oil and/or gas at the following location:

and you further agree to drill said Test Well with due diligence in a workmanlike manner to a depth sufficient to thoroughly test the following:

---

**Figure 3-2**—Farmout agreement. (From: *Landman's Encyclopedia,* 2nd Ed., R.L. Hankinson, Gulf Pub. Co., 1981.)

*(Figure 3-2 continued )*

(B) COMPLETION OR ABANDONMENT:  When the Test Well has reached its total depth, you agree:

(1) That if the Well can be completed as a producer of oil and/or gas to diligently prosecute the completion of said Well without unreasonable delays; or,

(2) If you determine to abandon the Well you will promptly furnish us with an appropriate electrical log acceptable to us and you further agree that you will not abandon the Well as a dry hole until you have furnished said electrical log to us and thereafter given us at least 48 hours notice of your intention to abandon, unless we consent to an earlier abandonment thereof.  After consent has been given, you agree to promptly plug and abandon the Test Well in accordance with all the requirements of any governmental body having jurisdiction.

## III FAILURE TO DRILL:

The only consequence of your failure to drill the proposed Test Well hereinabove provided for shall be the ipso facto cancellation of this Agreement in its entirety.

## IV COMMITMENT:

UPON WRITTEN REQUEST, and after completion of the Test Well provided for hereinabove in accordance with all the terms and provisions of this Agreement to our satisfaction, we agree:

## V INFORMATION AND REPORTS:

As a further express Consideration for this Agreement, and not as a covenant only, you agree to furnish to:

the following:

1. (a) DAILY DRILLING REPORTS on the progress of the well which shall include drilling depth, information on all tests including character, thickness, name of any formation penetrated, shows of oil, gas or water, and detailed reports on all drillstem tests.

(b) ____Certified Copies of all forms furnished to any governmental authority.

(c) ____Copies of all electrical logging surveys.

(d) ____Certified Copies of the well log upon completion.

(e) ____Certified Copies of the plugging record, if any.

(f) Samples of all cores and cuttings, if so requested.

2. Other Information Required:

*(Figure 3-2 continued on page 48.)*

*(Figure 3-2 continued )*

### VI PRODUCTION TESTS:

You agree to properly drillstem test any and all formations in which shows of oil and/or gas are encountered after notifying us of the proposed test and if we desire to be present during testing, you will delay such testing a reasonable amount of time in order to allow our representative to reach the well and witness the test, and you also agree to notify us immediately by telephone or telegraph as to the results of any such test. Notification shall be given to:

Name:
Address:
Telephone No.:
Night Telephone No.:

It is understood that our representatives shall have access to the rig floor at all times and to any and all information concerning the Test Well.

### VII DELAY RENTALS:

It is agreed that from and after the date of this Agreement we will pay any delay rentals which may become due on the Oil and Gas Leases subject to this Agreement until such time as the Assignment provided for in Section IV above has been executed, and thereafter bill you for_____of the delay rental paid by us.

### VIII CONSENT REQUIREMENT:

This Agreement is personal in nature and may not be assigned without our written consent being first obtained. When requesting consent to make an assignment of all or a portion of this Agreement you will advise the parties to whom the assignment will be made.

### IX STATUS OF PARTIES:

In the drilling of the Test Well and otherwise complying with the terms and provisions of this Agreement, you are acting independently of us and not as a partner in any capacity, mining or otherwise. We shall have no responsibility whatsoever in connection with the drilling of said well and it shall be drilled at your sole cost, risk and expense. You further agree to hold us harmless from any and all debts, claims or damages incurred in connection with the performance of this Agreement.

In regard to all provisions of this Agreement, it is understood and agreed that Time is of the Essence.

*(Figure 3-2 continued on page 49)*

*(Figure 3-2 continued )*

**X**  OTHER PROVISIONS:

       If the terms and provisions of this Agreement in its entirety are acceptable to you, will, you kindly indicate your approval by signing below in the space provided and re-turning_____executed copies of this Agreement to us within_____days. Failure to do so will result in the cancellation of this Agreement at our option.

This Agreement is APPROVED

and ACCEPTED this _____ day

of _____ , 19___ .

---

## What Is a Lease Play?

    Individuals or oil company exploration staffs will frequently develop ideas concerning the success potential of a specific geographic region. This area may be where little exploration or drilling activity has occurred in the past, or it could involve a heavily drilled region where leases have lapsed and where either new geological concepts or improved economic conditions warrant a renewed interest.

    Once a decision is reached to embark on a lease acquisition program (lease play) that covers an extensive area, the explora-tionists involved will order the necessary maps that indicate both surface (fee) ownership and any existing leases. A large area will be outlined on the land ownership map that broadly covers the region of interest. Brokers will be dispatched to acquire the desired leases. In the course of their work the brokers will frequently be instructed to verify ownership of mineral interest. The oil and gas rights on a property are carried by the mineral owner—who may or may not be the surface owner.

When a property is sold, the purchaser acquires the ownership of the surface and may or may not gain any of the mineral interests. This situation has been a source of great frustration to some property owners who willingly acquired their land without concern for the mineral rights, and discovered at a later date that the owner or lessee of the mineral interests has free access to the property to carry on any exploration or drilling activities that he wishes to engage in. A substantial oil or gas discovery only increases the anguish of the surface owner. However, he will be reimbursed for all land/crop damages to his property that are a result of the exploration and drilling operations.

## What Is an Oil and Gas Land Map?

The term *land map* refers to a variety of different graphical presentations, but in common usage it is a representation of an area in which surface (fee) ownership and existing oil and gas leases are indicated. The location of property or leases will be shown in most states (excluding Texas, parts of Louisiana, and the original 13 colonies) by tier, range, and section numbers (General Land Office Grid System). In Texas, the location of land is based on the registration of tracts in each county by survey name and abstract number. Commercial land maps in Texas commonly cover either one-quarter, one-half, or an entire county.

Surface ownership and oil and gas lease maps are commonly combined and can be ordered with various scales. The most common scales are: one inch equals one thousand feet (1″ = 1000′), one inch equals two thousand feet (1″ = 2000′), one inch equals four thousand feet (1″ = 4000′), and one inch equals one thousand varas (one vara equals 33.33 inches).

Cultural features commonly indicated on oil and gas land maps include cities, towns, highways, railways, bridges, cemetaries, oil and gas fields, pipelines, and plugged and abandoned wells. Rivers, large streams, and prominent hills and surface depressions will sometimes be shown also.

Different symbols are employed to indicate the location and status of the wells drilled in the mapped area. (See Figure 3-3.) The *total depth* (TD) reached in a well will frequently be shown, and possibly with a date if the well was plugged and abandoned. In addition to the total depth, there may also be listed a *plugged back total depth* (P, PB, or PBTD) to indicate that the lower part of the hole was sealed off and that subsequent testing occurred above that depth.

Occasionally, the depth at which different rock strata were reached will be shown. If the depth figures are prefixed by a minus sign, the numbers represent depths below sea level. If no minus sign is present, then the numbers represent the drilling depths at which the formations were reached in the well.

The operator (company or party responsible for the well) will have his name adjacent to the well symbol. The name of the well itself is commonly that of the lessor as taken from the lease covering the drill site. If more than one well is drilled by the operator on a lease, the wells are sequentially numbered. If one lease includes several noncontiguous tracts, wells on each separate tract will share the same letter designation followed by a well number (Jones A#1, A#2, B#1, B#2).

On any tract of land where an oil and gas lease is held, there are usually several different names shown on the corresponding land map. The fee owner will be designated, along with a survey name and sometimes a lessee name. If a well has been drilled on the acreage, the operator's name will be shown along with the well name if different from the indicated fee name. Figure 3-4 is a segment of an oil and gas lease map illustrating the symbolism normally employed to provide all necessary information.

(Number under well spots represents total depth)

$o^1$ Location

$\lozenge^1$ Abandoned location

$\diamondsuit^1$
$3881'$ Dry hole Temporary abandonment Suspended Operation with no well status report

$\diamondsuit^1$
J/A $3881'$ Junked & Abandoned well

$\bullet^1$
$3881'$ Oil well

$\bullet^1$
$3881'$ Abandoned oil producer

$\ominus^1$
$3881'$ Suspended operations Oil indicated

$\star^1$
$3881'$ Gas well

$\star^1$
$3881'$ Abandoned gas producer

$\star^1$
$3881'$ Suspended operations Gas indicated

$\star^1$
$3881'$ Gas & oil well

$\star^1$
$3881'$ Abandoned gas & oil producer

$\star^1$
$3881'$ Suspended operations Gas & oil indicated

$o^{1 WI}$ Water injection well Can be a location, old gas well, or an abandoned well

$o^{1 WS}$ Water supply Can be a location, old gas well, old oil, or an abandoned well

RE $o^1$ Reenter Any type of well Permission to do what he wants to the well with intent to complete

PB $o^1$ Plugback Plans only to plug the old well up with intent to complete

RC $o^1$ Recomplete Plans only to recomplete well in same zone by means of a different method

WO $o^1$ Workover (Basically the same as recomplete)

DD $o^1$ Drilled deeper Has permission to drill an old hole deeper with intent to complete

L.Davis
100ac. Fee ownership and tract size

R.SMITH
A-1902 Survey name and abstract number

———— Section boundary (light line)

▬▬▬▬ Survey boundary (heavy line)

39 Section number

✗ Same fee ownership (half arrows)

✗ Same lessee (full arrows)

Gulf
1-20-85 Lessee and date of lease expiration

**Figure 3-3**—Well symbols legend. (From: Petroleum Information Corporation, Heydrick Map Services, San Antonio, TX 78217.)

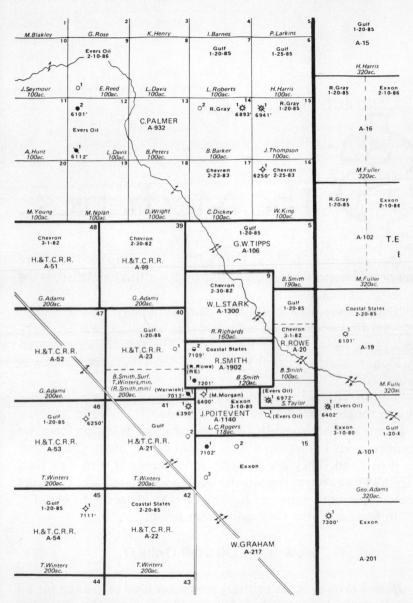

**Figure 3-4**—Oil and gas lease map segment. (From: Petroleum Information Corporation, Heydrick Map Services, San Antonio, TX 78217.)

# Chapter Four

# $ The Mechanics

The scene: back table at Don's Olive Pit, a topless bar where weary businessmen congregate to sip a few drinks and discuss the different news topics.

"I don't know Duane, maybe you're right, maybe we should go out and find our own oil well. We sure wouldn't have to worry about long lines at the service station." These words were slurred by Don, who always drank heavily whenever the energy crisis was discussed.

"I mean, after all, a zillion wells have been drilled, so it couldn't be too tough. How do you think it's done?"

Duane looked thoughtful and, as he flicked dead flies from the counter, said "I don't know how it's done here, but in China they do it by hand. They get an army of workers out, and they start diggin'! Of course, at the top the well's a half-mile wide. They just keep diggin until someone hollars, 'RUN, it's going to blow!'

"In Russia, I hear they use a laser beam. . . ."

## How Is an Oil Well Drilled?

*Rotary drilling* is the primary technique used in drilling for oil and gas in the United States. A drilling bit is attached to a column of tubular steel drill pipe, and the resultant *drill string* and bit are rotated under an applied weight. The bit has projections that grind against a rock surface to fragment and disintegrate it. Pressure on the drill bit is supplied by the drill pipe itself in combination with *drill collars.* (Drill collars are approximately thirty-feet long and weigh more than standard drill pipe. They are attached directly above the bit and in addition to their added weight also provide greater rigidity to the lower part of the drill string.)

Drill pipe commonly comes in approximately thirty-foot lengths, called *joints,* and a segment comprising two or three joints is called a *stand.* As a well is being drilled, joints of drill pipe are added continuously at the surface as the hole deepens. The connection between each added joint and the continuous string of drill pipe in the hole is a tapered screw fitting (tool joint) between thread and coupling connections.

The drill string is turned by the rotation of the *rotary table,* which in turn is powered by the drilling unit power plant. The connection between the rotary table and the drill pipe is provided by the *kelly,* a square or hexagonal cross-sectioned joint of steel pipe, connected to the drill string, that slips freely up and down through a similarily shaped opening in the center of the rotary table.

The derrick of a drilling rig is the trademark that forms the backdrop for most settings depicting the oil industry. Its primary purpose is to provide the added elevation required to lower or lift joints or stands of drill pipe into or out of the hole during various operations (when a bit change is required or during logging of a well). The derrick also provides a convenient storage facility for stands of drill pipe and collar. Figure 4-1 shows a typical rotary drilling rig.

Drilling mud is employed in most rotary drilling operations. The flow into the well and back forms a continuous circuit with additional mud being added as the hole deepens. The mud provides a number of services that range from lubricating the bit

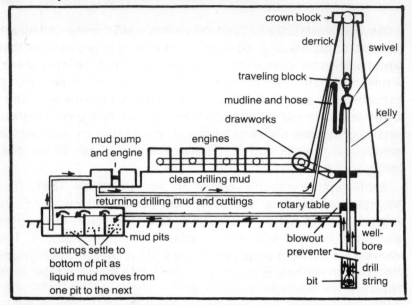

**Figure 4-1**—A rotary drilling rig. (From: *Introduction to Petroleum Production*, Vol. 1, D.R. Skinner, Gulf Pub. Co., 1981.)

to transporting rock fragments from the bottom of the hole to the surface. At the surface, the mud flows across a screen that effectively filters the rock fragments from the mud.

The weight of the mud is a critical factor in any drilling operation. Fluids within the earth undergo increased compression with depth. Failure to counterbalance *formation pressure* while drilling will result in a *blowout*, where the mud is forced from the hole with accompanying fluids and gases. The hazard of fire in this situation is great, and a loss of life is not uncommon. For this reason, the total weight of the drilling mud in the hole should exceed any anticipated formation pressures. When mud weight is inadequate, natural gas may develop a large bubble in the mud system that will continue up the hole until overlying mud weight is incapable of containing the gas. At this stage, the well will "kick" with the passage of gas to the surface and force overlying mud out of the hole. This situation has apparently caused some overweight drillers to shatter long-distance sprint records. Slower people and trees have been flattened in their path.

An easy remedy to the problem is simply to drill wells with mud that has been weighed down by mixing with heavy substances. This remedy, however, is not a satisfactory solution, as too heavy a mud will both impede the drilling operation and likely inflict extensive damage on the zones in which oil or gas is being sought. If the gas or fluid pressure in a formation is significantly less than the pressure caused by the weight of the mud column, then the mud will flow into the formation and impair production of the hydrocarbon reservoir.

In some regions *lost circulation* is a common problem and can be both hazardous to a well and also difficult to control. In general, circulation refers to the circuit that the drilling fluid makes from ground surface to drill bit and back again to the surface. When a highly porous and permeable formation (a *fractured* or *broken formation)* is encountered, then there is a tendency for the drilling fluids (mud or water) to enter the rock body. A small fluid loss is common in most wells. However, when a large quantity of fluid is lost and continues to drain from the well bore into the formation, then that formation is referred to as a *lost circulation zone.* The loss of drilling mud is expensive; but more important, the loss of the drilling mud reduces the weight of the mud column in the well bore. This weight loss could lead to a blowout. To counteract lost circulation, a variety of substances are pumped into the well. Peanut shells, cotton seeds, cellophane, and similar materials are circulated in the mud system to provide a physical blockage in the zone where fluid is being lost. In some wells lost circulation has been so severe and costly that the wells were abandoned.

All facets of a drilling operation are important and require constant attention. A petroleum engineer or drilling engineer will oversee the mechanical operation and ensure the smooth performance of a drilling program. The *tool pusher* and drillers will ensure an efficient and continued performance of the drilling crews.

A drilling operation is a 24-hour, seven-day-a-week continuous program from the time of *spudding* (starting of a well) to TD (total depth, when a well has reached its projected depth). In addition to the regular drilling and engineering staff, a mud engineer will periodically visit the site to verify that the drilling fluid is maintaining its desired properties, and a geologist or mud logger will be present to examine rock samples and look for oil and gas indications. Assorted tourists, visiting dignitaries, and lost travelers may also be found on and around drilling wells.

## What Is Meant by a "Show"?

In any oil or gas well-drilling operation great attention is paid to any information obtained from a well that indicates the presence of oil or gas. "Sniffing" the samples that come out of the hole is a standard procedure that dates back to the infancy of the business. Both oil and natural gas have characteristic odors that can be "smelled" when present in sufficient quantities. If an odor is detected in the samples, then the *show* is recorded by the driller or a well site geologist, along with the depth at which it was encountered.

The most common identification of shows is based on the examination of *cuttings* (rock fragments carried to the surface by the drilling unit's mud system). The presence of oil on these samples may sometimes by viewed directly with the unaided eye, as when the rock chips have an evident oil film coating. More commonly, the samples are viewed at the well site under ultraviolet light, which causes oil to "fluoresce" (glow with a gold, yellow, or orange color). These cuttings are then treated with a solvent such as carbon tetrachloride or even lighter fluid to separate any movable oil from the rock fragments. If oil can be observed (it's normally easier to see when viewed under ultraviolet light) separating from the rock chips, then that sample is described as having a *cut*. Adjectives such as strong, good, or weak are frequently used to describe a cut.

In many drilling operations a *mud logger* is employed to examine the well cuttings as they arrive at the surface. His examination will include a description of the rock type being drilled, and an explanation of all shows that have been encountered. An integral part of his equipment will be a gas detector connected to the drilling rig mud system. As gas is encountered at the bottom of the hole, it will be carried upward in the mud. On reaching the surface, it will be automatically recorded for both its quantity and composition. The time required for mud or rock cuttings to be transported from the bottom of the well to the surface is called *lag time*. This interval can be easily calculated and must be known to establish the depth from which a particular sample came.

The mud logger will maintain a close vigil on all shows. If they are highly encouraging, drilling activities may be suspended while a zone is tested.

In any geological evaluation that leads to the selection of a drill site, a great deal of attention is paid to any shows that have been reported in neighboring wells. These are the direct indicators that oil or gas are present and that the area warrants close study.

## What Is Meant by Logging?

The observations of the well site geologist or mud logger are usually recorded on continuous strips or rolls of paper with pertinent data shown adjacent to the corresponding drilling depth. The appropriate symbols for different rock types are frequently shown on this type of log, over the intervals which they occur. Figure 4-2 shows the results of a logging operation.

When a well has reached its projected depth, then one or a series of sensitive electronic or mechanical devices are lowered by wire line (cable) into the well. This operation can occur in either an *open hole* (the measuring devices are in direct contact with the rock through which they pass) or a *cased hole* (measuring devices are lowered into the hole after casing has been set).

Open hole logging can be undertaken at any time during drilling, but it is normally delayed until the well has reached its projected depth. (It has been said that "a normal logging operation is an undisciplined meeting of bewildered people at a muddy well site at two o'clock in the morning.") The purpose of the logging is to determine if the various rocks penetrated in the well contain hydrocarbons. If oil or gas is present, it is necessary

| Depth | Driller's log | Cuttings analysis | Gamma ray | Resist. | Conclusion |
|-------|---------------|-------------------|-----------|---------|------------|
| 4810 | hard drilling | shale/clay | | | |
| 4820 | medium | clay | | | |
| 4830 | hard | limestone | | | dry |
| 4840 | | | | | |
| 4850 | | | | | |
| 4860 | medium | sandstone | | | oil or gas |
| 4870 | | | | | |
| 4880 | hard | shale | | | |
| 4890 | soft | sand & lime | | | oil, gas, water |
| 4900 | | | | | |
| 4910 | | | | | |
| 4920 | medium | shale | | | |
| 4930 | hard | dolomite | | | oil or water |
| 4940 | hard | shale | | | total depth |

**Figure 4-2**—Results of a logging operation. (From: *Introduction to Petroleum Production,* Vol. 1, D.R. Skinner, Gulf Pub. Co., 1981.)

that some estimate be made as to whether either or both can be commercially produced.

The three basic properties of rocks that are interpreted with an open hole log are water saturation, porosity, and permeability (only in a qualitative sense).

## Resistivity Logging

The determination of water saturation permits the calculation of the rock volume occupied by oil or gas. Saline water, the normal liquid constituent of rocks located at varying depths below the earth's surface, is a good conductor of electrical current, while both oil and natural gas are poor conductors. Consequently, the first log run following the drilling of a well measures the rock's conductivity. (*Resistivity* is the reciprocal of conductivity. It is traditionally employed to describe the passage of an electric current through a rock body.)

In scanning this first log particular attention is paid to all rock units that indicate a high resistivity (low conductivity), as this low current flow can be caused by either the presence of oil or gas. The presence of "fresh" water (fresh or brackish water, because of low salt content, will also be a poor conductor of electrical current) or a dense rock body in which relatively little fluid is present will also result in a high resistivity.

Additional logs are then commonly run to evaluate porosity in those zones that demonstrated a high resistivity. Well logging can be very expensive, and thus the less logging required, the less costly the program. Many companies offer open hole logging services, and a variety of instruments are available to provide different information.

## Porosity Logging

After running the resistivity log, it is common to run a log that can be related to either a rock's porosity or permeability. *Porosity* is the percentage of a rock body that is occupied by pores or voids. In an oil or gas reservoir, porosity is the percentage of a rock unit occupied by fluids (oil, water, or gas). An estimate of porosity based on log data is therefore an estimate of the storage capabilities of a formation. The greater the porosity of a rock, the more water, oil, or gas it will contain.

Logging devices that are designed to provide information on porosity enable one to determine the volume of liquid or gas. The instrument itself may be designed to measure the transmission of sound waves (sonic log, acoustic velocity log) in differing formations, or the effect of neutron (neutron log) or gamma (density log) bombardment as the logging instrument (logging tool) is pulled up the hole. The type of porosity device employed in a well will hinge on the experience of the operator or well site geologist in determining which is best suited for the particular region.

## Permeability Logging

*Permeability* is a measure of how efficiently a fluid or gas will flow through a rock body. The greater a rock's permeability, the greater its ability to yield liquids or gas into the well bore and to the surface of the earth. This property is a measure of how well the pore spaces are connected in a formation. A rock body such as shale or clay has very low inherent permeability and thus makes a very poor oil or gas reservoir. Oil or gas may be present, but they cannot be commercially extracted.

The cause of good permeability is either a good connection in the basic network of pores in the rock or fractures or breaks within the rock body. All oil and gas fields characterized by wells with high daily production have reservoirs with high permeability.

Permeability can be detected with several different types of open hole logs. When a mud is employed in the drilling of a well, there is a tendency for this mud to enter any zone that has porosity and permeability. This infiltration occurs because the weight of the mud column in the well bore is greater than the pressure of any liquids or gas in the formation, and thus any liquids or gases will be pushed back into the rock. As the drilling mud seeks to enter the formation, the rock itself acts as a filter and retains the mud solids (filter cake or mud cake) on the face of the formation, while the associated fluid (filtrate) passes into the zone. The net effect is that this mud cake develops on porous and permeable zones and can be detected by open hole logs specifically designed for that purpose.

## The Decision to "Complete or Abandon"

When the logging is completed, the "head scratching" begins. A decision must be made to either plug and abandon the well or to attempt to complete it as an oil or gas producer. The responsible parties will review all data accumulated during the drilling and logging operations. All oil or gas shows encountered in the well, and any drill stem test information, will be included in this analysis.

A review of the combined information will provide a strong incentive either for plugging or for completion. In a significant number of wells a definite conclusion cannot be reached, and either additional drill stem tests are performed or a decision to plug or complete is made, leaving some questions unanswered.

If a well is to be completed, then a string of production casing is set. This continuous column of hollow steel is lowered into the hole with each 31.5-foot section being screwed on to the pipe below it as it enters the well bore. The length of the string is increased in this fashion until it extends below the zone to be tested.

Cement is then pumped into the hole to fill up the space between the outside of the casing and the exposed wall of the hole. It is essential that this cavity be completely filled over the zone to be tested and for several hundred feet above and below the zone. The cement effectively isolates each rock unit exposed in the well bore; thus liquids and gases cannot communicate or pass from zone to zone.

When the cement has hardened, the well is ready for testing. At this stage, cased hole logs are run to verify the efficiency of the cement in filling up the necessary portion of the well bore. In addition, these logs will confirm the depth at which the selected test formation occurs.

## What Happens When a Well Is Cored?

In the drilling of a well it is often desirable to view and to perform measurements on large portions of rock rather than on the small cuttings transported by the mud system. Reservoir engineers prefer large rock samples, because they are then able to accurately determine factors such as rock composition, porosity, and permeability which enables them to pass judgment on potential reservoir merit.

In regions where well information is scarce, companies will frequently program a large number of cores. Their instructions to the well site geologist or mud logger may be to "circulate bottoms up" on all "drilling breaks" and to cut cores where shows are present. A "drilling break" refers to a faster than usual drilling rate that results when increased porosity is encountered in a rock body. For example: A well is drilling at the rate of four minutes per foot, and then penetration increases to one minute per foot. At this stage, instructions are relayed to the driller to stop drilling and to circulate. The drill pipe continues to turn in the hole without actually drilling, and the mud circulates through the system until the most recent cuttings in the bottom of the hole are carried to the surface (bottoms up). When the samples reach the surface, they will be analyzed for evidence of oil or gas. If no shows are evident, instructions will be given to resume drilling.

If the samples do indicate the presence of oil or gas, the decision may be to cut a *core*. When this decision is reached, the entire string of drill pipe is removed from the hole, stacked in the derrick, and the drill bit is then replaced by a *core bit and barrel*. The core barrel is 30-60 feet long and is connected to the core bit, which provides the cutting surface that penetrates the rock. The rotary motion of the core bit will result in a downward cutting along the margins of the rock surface, thus forcing a narrow column of rock (core) into the retaining barrel.

After the core has been cut over the prescribed thickness, the entire string of drill pipe with the attached core barrel will be brought to the surface. The core will be removed, described, closely examined, and tested for any water, oil, or gas content. Porosity and permeability values will be determined for specific intervals along the core to determine reservoir potential. The information obtained from this core will later be incorporated with log data in evaluating the oil and gas potential of the well.

When a well has reached its projected depth, and the open hole logging has been completed, it is frequently necessary to obtain additional information on specific zones in the well. One means of gathering more data is to collect *sidewall cores*. In this operation specific points are designated on the open hole logs where the sidewall cores are to be obtained. A core gun is lowered by cable into the well bore, and core barrels are fired into the well wall at the selected points.

After firing, each barrel and core is recovered by a retrieving cable which is attached to the back of each core barrel. When the sidewall cores are brought to the surface, they are examined for oil, gas, and water content and subjected to tests to determine porosity and permeability. A report is then prepared that indicates the depth at which each sidewall core was taken and the results of all analyses.

## How Is a Well Tested?

The initial testing of a well may occur during the actual drilling operations. If a zone is encountered that has encouraging shows, it is often preferable to test at that time rather than when the well has reached its projected depth.

A *drill stem test* (DST) is the common procedure for evaluating a formation prior to casing being set in the hole. In this operation the drill pipe is removed from the hole, and the drill bit is replaced with a *test tool.* The tool is attached to the drill pipe and lowered into the well until it reaches the depth to be tested. Situated above the test tool is a *packer* which can be expanded by a controlled motion of the drill pipe at the surface. Expansion of the packer results in sealing off of the zone to be tested from the remainder of the hole above it. If the well has been drilled to a depth significantly below the zone to be tested, a *straddle packer* is employed. This packer seals the zone off from both the upper and lower parts of the hole, isolating a narrow interval for the test.

When the packer or packers are in place, the tool will be opened, and any liquids or gases in the formation will flow into the tool and up the drill pipe. The tool will be opened and closed for selected time intervals, and recorders incorporated in the instrument will provide information on all pressure changes in the formation.

After the test is completed and the drill pipe is pulled from the hole, careful attention is directed to any fluids contained in the pipe. The drill pipe is separated into stands (two or three joints depending on the height of the derrick) and stacked upright in the derrick until the test tool is retrieved. The recovery on a DST may be a drill string filled with gas, oil, or saltwater—or it might contain only minor quantities of gas, oil, water, or drilling mud.

At the surface, the pressure recorders are taken from the test tool and analyzed. This information is employed initially to determine if the test was a mechanical success. A packer may not have held or the pressure recording devices may have malfunctioned, and thus another test will be required. If the test is valid, the pressure variations are measured, and an estimate of formation permeability is derived. Following the test, the drill bit is reconnected to the drill string and lowered into the hole to resume drilling operations.

The results of a DST can be critical in establishing the oil or gas merit of a particular zone in a well. The use of straddle packers in bracketing an interval incorporates more mechanical risks then does a conventional DST. For this reason, it is desirable to run the test as soon as a prospective zone is reached. If the drilling is continued for an extended depth below the interval, a straddle packer assembly will be required.

When a well has been drilled to its projected depth, logged, and the decision is made to test, the first step is to *set casing* in the open hole to a depth below which the tests will be conducted. The casing is tubular steel, commonly in 31.5-foot lengths, and usually with a 4.5- or 5.5-inch internal diameter. The individual lengths (joints) of casing are screwed together and lowered into the well to form a continuous conduit from the surface down to the test zone.

To isolate specific zones in a well, it is necessary that cement be pumped into the hole and allowed to set between the hole wall and the casing. This procedure effectively separates the different rock units from each other, allowing no fluids to migrate from zone to zone within the well.

A *perforating gun* is then lowered by cable into the casing to a depth where the unit to be tested is located. Shots are fired within the casing that penetrate both the steel and the cement before dissipating into the formation. A series of conduits are now open between the potential reservoir and the casing, which in turn extends to the surface.

If the reservoir has high pressures and good porosity and permeability, the contained fluids may attempt to flow up the casing to the surface. For this reason, the casing is commonly loaded (filled) with water or mud prior to the perforating.

If the well has no apparent response to the perforations, the well will be *swabbed* (a disc will be lowered by cable into the casing or tubing below the level of the fluid and then drawn out). The raising of the swab creates a suction which forces a portion of the fluid to the surface. The goal is to reduce the weight of the fluid in the hole to the point where the natural formation pressure will overcome the weight of the mud or water remaining in the casing. Swabbing of the column of fluid will continue until the liquids or gases in the formation are free to flow. Sometimes, a well will be swabbed completely dry without any positive response.

If a well will not flow naturally or only in small quantities, it is commonly because of blocked perforations or a low porosity or permeability in the reservoirs. In this situation acid is pumped into the well at a sufficient pressure to penetrate the formation. The acid is allowed to remain in the well for a short period of time and, if the well will still not flow, it is then swabbed out.

If the zone being tested is a carbonate rock, such as limestone or dolomite, a large quantity of acid may be pumped into the formation under high pressure. The known chemical reaction between the acid and this type of rock is a partial dissolution of the carbonate and the consequent development of improved porosity and permeability. This chemical treatment is commonly referred to as an *acid frac* (fracture). After the acid has been permitted to react for a prescribed period of time, the well is opened and the fluid is allowed to flow back to the surface. If the well will not flow naturally at this stage, swabbing will be continued until it does flow or until the zone is deemed unproductive and abandoned.

If fracing is required in sandstone reservoirs, fluids, along with a *propping agent,* are pumped at very high pressure into the formation. This agent forces a breakdown of the rock surrounding the well bore over the interval being tested. The propping agent is usually a mixture of various sizes of sand grains that enter the formation with the introduced fluids and it thus serves to keep zones separated where partings have occurred.

After a well has been fraced, it is allowed to flow until it has cleaned up. The bulk of the frac fluids introduced into the well will be recovered in the days following the operation. Full recovery of all the fluids is uncommon.

Fracturing a reservoir can cost less than $20,000 or many hundreds of thousands of dollars. Consequently, major frac jobs on a reservoir are not entered into lightly.

# Chapter Five

# $ The People

Few industries provide the diversity of professions found in a major oil company. If investors are included, the oil industry approaches a total representation in all fields of human endeavor. It is a highly diversified giant relying totally on the industry of its employees and the benevolence of its supporters.

The oil business is doomed as a petroleum searching and producing enterprise. Barring a premature demise occasioned by a nuclear holocaust, oil's effect as the major energy supplier will begin to diminish in the early stages of the twenty-first century. It will be a lingering memory at the close of that century with the few remaining oil reserves being employed in petrochemical and new, allied industries. During the cosmic gasp that marked its existence the oil seekers will have arrived, learned, endured, and been forgotten. To borrow a thought from the inscription on Sir Isaac Newton's tomb, "Stand in awe mortals, you will not see their kind again."

## Who Is the Operator of a Well?
## What Are His Responsibilities?

The operator is an organization or individual who manages and has the responsibility for all technical decisions related to the drilling and testing of a well. He may be aided in his work by an *operating committee* composed of members from different organizations with a vested interest in the well or program. His authority is defined in a *joint operating agreement* (JOA) approved by the different participants, or their representatives, in the venture. His task is to ensure that the agreed upon program is carried out in both a professional and fiscally responsible fashion. One of his many functions is to provide *drilling reports* to the investors that will account for the daily operation of the venture.

Before the initiation of a well, the operator will be responsible for assuring that all technical operations leading to the selection of a site have been completed. This responsibility includes all lease and legal matters relating to the drill site and might involve the overseeing of a geophysical program or an in-depth study of subsurface geological trends. It is then his task to assure that all necessary state and federal requirements are fulfilled prior to drilling.

The operator is the premier authority on a well, although he is restricted in various activities if he is not the sole participant in the venture. Most drilling operations involve several and frequently many investors. Decisions such as testing, coring or, even more important, the plugging or attempts to complete a well almost always require the concurrence of the investors or their representatives. There are provisions in all joint operating agreements that provide some "out" for a participant not wishing to be unwillingly committed to an expensive course of action.

"Operations" is a synonym for headache. To be an operator requires a capable organization with access to talented personnel. The mismanagement of a well can result in great financial loss to its backers. When an operator's competence is in question, there are standard provisions in most joint operating agreements that provide for his removal and replacement.

The benefits that accrue to an operator, aside from his leadership position and his decision-making role, are minor and hardly counterbalance the weight of his responsibilities. In addition to his other duties, it is his task to provide a reliable estimate of all costs involved in a particular program. This cost appraisal is normally submitted in the form of an *authorization for expenditures* (AFE) in which all cost items are tabulated with estimates of the amount to be expended. A standard form will list the well name, its location, proposed depth, and all estimated costs associated with the well.

In the breakdown of costs all estimated expenses are listed along with a designation of either costs to casing point or completion costs. Costs to casing point are frequently referred to as "dry hole" costs. These are the expenses incurred up to the point where a decision is made to either plug and abandon the well or to attempt a completion. Expenses in this category include all the costs related to the drilling of the well with drilling rig time, location preparation, rig fuel, drilling fluids, open hole logging, and surface casing as the major items. If drill stem testing or coring is anticipated, an estimate of these costs is also included.

If after viewing the open hole logs a decision is reached to attempt a completion, additional costs are incurred. These potential completion costs are routinely included on most AFE's. The major costs items in this phase of the operation are the production casing, rig time, cement, cased hole logs, and various treatments performed on the well.

Add together the cost to casing point and completion costs, and the result is a rough estimate of the total exposure of the investors. Events will conspire to make the initial AFE a caricature of the final costs in most wells.

The AFE is routinely prepared and circulated for approval by all participants in a venture with the understanding that these figures are only estimates. Cost overruns are the rule rather than the exception, and thus most experienced investors are accustomed to "digging a little deeper." Figure 5-1 is an AFE.

It is because of the unpredictability of many cost items that some operators elect to go the *turnkey route*. In a turnkey drilling program an agreement is made with a drilling contractor to drill a well to a specified depth for a fixed price. This agreement usually costs more than an *invoiced program,* as the drilling contractor is accepting the mechanical risks of getting a well down which are usually assumed by the working interest participants.

**AUTHORITY FOR EXPENDITURE**

DATE

| COUNTY | DISTRICT | LEASE WELL OR FACILITY NAME | A. F. E. NO. |
|---|---|---|---|

DESCRIPTION OF WORK TO BE PERFORMED

ESTIMATED STARTING DATE      ESTIMATED COMPLETION DATE

| TYPE OF JOB | OWNERS | % INTEREST NET | WI. | ESTIMATED COST |
|---|---|---|---|---|
| ___ NEW DRILLING | | | | |
| ___ DEVELOPMENT DRILLING | | | | |
| ___ LEASE OR WELL EQUIP. | | | | |
| ___ LEASE ACQUISITION | | | | |
| ___ WORKOVERS, REPAIRS | | | | |
| ___ OTHER (DESCRIBE) | TOTAL | | | |
| | DENOTE OPERATOR | | | |

| ITEM AND DESCRIPTION | QUANTITY | UNIT PRICE | TOTAL COST | DRY HOLE |
|---|---|---|---|---|
| INTANGIBLE DRILLING COST: | | | | |
| Labor, Company & Contract | | | | |
| Fuel, Water, Power & Lubricants | | | | |
| Hauling | | | | |
| Roads, Location,& Contract | | | | |
| Contract Drilling | | | | |
| Day Work | | | | |
| Drilling Bits | | | | |
| Compressor & Tool Rentals | | | | |
| Pulling Unit or Cable Tools | | | | |
| Mud & Chemicals | | | | |
| Mud Logger | | | | |
| Cement & Cementing | | | | |
| Coring | | | | |
| Well Surveys (Logging, etc.) | | | | |
| Drill Stem Test | | | | |
| Perforating | | | | |
| Treating | | | | |
| Supplies & Miscellaneous | | | | |
| Total Intangible Drilling Costs | | | | |
| | | | | |
| TANGIBLE DRILLING COSTS: | | | | |
| Casing (conductor) | | | | |
| Casing (surface) | | | | |
| Casing (intermediate) | | | | |
| Casing (production) | | | | |
| Tubing | | | | |
| Packer (s) | | | | |
| Rods, Sucker | | | | |
| Pumping Unit | | | | |
| Electric Motor | | | | |
| Engine | | | | |
| Subsurface Pump | | | | |
| Well Head | | | | |
| Total Tangible Drilling Costs | | | | |
| | | | | |
| LEASE EQUIPMENT & INSTALLATION: | | | | |
| Tank, Storage | | | | |
| Treater | | | | |
| Heater | | | | |
| Meter Run | | | | |
| Separator | | | | |
| Line Pipe | | | | |
| Miscellaneous Connections | | | | |
| Trucking and Labor | | | | |
| Total Lease Equipment, etc. | | | | |
| | | | | |
| TOTAL AFE COST | | | | |

| PARTNER APPROVAL | APPROVAL | NAME | DATE |
|---|---|---|---|
| | ESTIMATED BY | | |
| FOR: | | | |
| BY: | | | |
| DATE: | FINAL APPROVAL | | |

**Figure 5-1**—Authority For Expenditure form.

During a drilling program the operator receives a fee (the amount is spelled out in the JOA) for the time actually spent in drilling. For example, it may be stated in the JOA that the operator will receive $1500/month during drilling operations. If the drilling rig is on location for 20 days, the fee will amount to $1000. In addition, there is a provision in the JOA stating that for each producing well the operator will receive some sum of money. Most JOA's show a monthly per-well sum between $200 and $400. All investors would be well-advised to review the joint operating agreement prior to participating in a venture. A close review of this document can prevent some unpleasant surprises later on. Figure 5-2 is a table of contents for a JOA.

Most joint operating agreements are based on a model form prepared by the American Association of Petroleum Landmen (AAPL). All facets relating to a drilling operation are included in this document. The total agreement, in conjunction with its attached accounting procedure, is precisely worded and usually quite lengthy.

There are specific statements in this document where options are present and insertions by the operator are necessarily made. It is strongly advised that any working interest participant in a drilling program review this agreement and pay particular attention to any modification or amendments to the basic form.

## Who Is an Explorationist?

The term "explorationist" is collectively applied to all individuals who devote a significant part of their energies to the search for oil or gas. This designation includes a diversity of professions and talents and especially those individuals who lack formal training and developed their wisdom the "hard way."

The science of "looking for oil" is relatively new, as the first oil well only dates back to 1859. Colonel Drake earned the glory of making that initial discovery at a depth of 69 feet with a well located near Titusville, Pennsylvania. As the use of oil expanded, especially for transportation, an increased effort was directed toward its location and recovery.

Initial seekers employed a follow-the-leader pattern. If an oil well was discovered near a graveyard, other searchers would lease and drill near graveyards. After a while, the early explorationists began to see a pattern of rock behavior in areas where oil had been located, and they were thus able to employ some science in their search.

Geology, the science of the earth, was the natural field in which to continue and improve on the work done by early oil pioneers. Tens of thousands of petroleum specialists have studied geology and geophysics with the continued search for oil and gas as their primary professional emphasis. This professional group now represents a major percentage of explorationists.

Other professionals commonly associated with oil and gas exploration are petroleum landmen and petroleum engineers. Exploration is not their particular interest, since they are specialized in other functions. However, the "lure to look" is infectious and, through their constant association with oil deals and the excitement of the business, many of these professionals gravitate into the exploration field.

ARTICLE                      TITLE

    I.  DEFINITIONS

   II.  EXHIBITS

  III.  INTERESTS OF PARTIES
        A.  OIL AND GAS INTERESTS
        B.  INTEREST OF PARTIES IN COSTS AND PRODUCTION

  IV.  TITLES
        A.  TITLE EXAMINATION
        B.  LOSS OF TITLE
           1.  Failure of Title
           2.  Loss by Non-Payment or Erroneous Payment of Amount Due
           3.  Other Losses

   V.  OPERATOR
        A.  DESIGNATION AND RESPONSIBILITIES OF OPERATOR
        B.  RESIGNATION OR REMOVAL OF OPERATOR AND SELECTION OF SUCCESSOR
           1.  Resignation or Removal of Operator
           2.  Selection of Successor Operator

**Figure 5-2**—Contents of a Joint Operating Agreement.

*(Figure 5-2 continued )*

      C.  EMPLOYEES
      D.  DRILLING CONTRACTS

VI.  DRILLING AND DEVELOPMENT
      A.  INITIAL WELL
      B.  SUBSEQUENT OPERATIONS
          1.  Proposed Operations
          2.  Operations by Less than All Parties
      C.  RIGHT TO TAKE PRODUCTION IN KIND
      D.  ACCESS TO CONTRACT AREA AND INFORMATION
      E.  ABANDONMENT OF WELLS
          1.  Abandonment of Dry Holes
          2.  Abandonment of Wells that have Produced

VII.  EXPENDITURES AND LIABILITY OF PARTIES
      A.  LIABILITY OF PARTIES
      B.  LIENS AND PAYMENT DEFAULTS
      C.  PAYMENTS AND ACCOUNTING
      D.  LIMITATION OF EXPENDITURES
          1.  Drill or Deepen
          2.  Rework or Plug Back
          3.  Other Operations
      E.  ROYALTIES, OVERRIDING ROYALTIES AND OTHER PAYMENTS
      F.  RENTALS, SHUT-IN WELL PAYMENTS AND MINIMUM ROYALTIES
      G.  TAXES
      H.  INSURANCE

VIII.  ACQUISITION, MAINTENANCE OR TRANSFER OF INTEREST
      A.  SURRENDER OF LEASES
      B.  RENEWAL OR EXTENSION OF LEASES
      C.  ACREAGE OR CASH CONTRIBUTION
      D.  SUBSEQUENTLY CREATED INTEREST
      E.  MAINTENANCE OF UNIFORM INTEREST
      F.  WAIVER OF RIGHT TO PARTITION
      G.  PREFERENTIAL RIGHT TO PURCHASE

IX.  INTERNAL REVENUE CODE ELECTION

X.  CLAIMS AND LAWSUITS

XI.  FORCE MAJEURE

XII.  NOTICES

XIII.  TERM OF AGREEMENT

XIV.  COMPLIANCE WITH LAWS AND REGULATIONS
      A.  LAWS, REGULATIONS AND ORDERS
      B.  GOVERNING LAW

XV.  OTHER PROVISIONS
XVI.  MISCELLANEOUS

Success in oil and gas exploration requires good business judgment and common sense, regardless of professional background or degrees of education. Anyone can play the game, but some success is required to stay at the table.

### Who Is an Investor?

The key to any business is the person who supplies the necessary capital for the continuation and growth of a specified program. The oil business would be in a sad state if investors' funds were to dry up, and the burden of total cost liability had to be carried by individual operators or organizations. The decline in the rate of drilling would be matched only by the increased ranks at the unemployment office.

Companies that make solicitations for specific programs develop an extensive client list that grows or diminishes depending on the degree of success in preceding ventures. Such a list is closely guarded, as it is the heart of an oil company's operation. It is a tabulation of individuals who have demonstrated their interest in the oil business in the most sincere fashion . . . money.

In part, the willingness to invest personal funds in an oil exploration program is related to the tax shelter opportunities incorporated therein. Tax advantages in oil and gas drilling are the primary motivation for investors with large tax liabilities (50-75% tax rate). Investors less financially endowed also receive this benefit, though not in the proper proportion to warrant the capital risk. But the primary basis for small-investor participation in the oil business must relate to adventure and profit. By accepting this criterion, most citizens are candidates for oil deals with only their financial shortcomings or inherent suspicions curbing their willingness.

A common approach to enter the business at a nominal cost is the *federal filing* or *lottery* now conducted on a bimonthly basis in several states. The Bureau of Land Management (BLM) determines periodically which federal lands will be available in an upcoming drawing. A bulletin issued by the BLM provides the location and size of the offered leases, along with a lease identification number. Figure 5-3 is a synopsis of the simultaneous filing procedure.

On the designated date, a winner and two runner-up cards are drawn from a bin in which all applications for a particular tract have been placed. The winner is contacted, and he then has 30 days in which to claim his prize and to pay the first-year rental ($1 per acre) on the lease.

The winner of a lottery (there may be several hundred winners in a drawing session) is then the proud possessor of a lease with a value that ranges somewhere between "bonanza" and "heartburn." The holder of a highly sought after tract will be rewarded

### SIMULTANEOUS FILING ON FEDERAL LEASES

1. At 10:00 a.m. on the 3rd Monday of alternate months the various state offices of the Interior Department's Bureau of Land Management (BLM) posts a list of those tracts of land that for a period of 15 business days are open for receipt of applications to lease.

2. Applications for each tract must be made on the BLM's Simultaneous Oil and Gas Drawing Entry Card (Bureau Form 3112-1).

3. Each Simultaneous Entry Card must be accompanied by a filing fee of $10 payable to the BLM.

4. All Simultaneous Entry Cards received during the posted period are placed in a box or drum and a public drawing is held; the BLM has replaced this system in some of its offices with an electronic drawing system.

5. The applicant represented by the first Simultaneous Entry Card drawn on each tract is entitled to a 10-year oil and gas lease on the acreage covered by such tract upon payment of the first year's annual rental of $1 per acre. The BLM will send to each successful applicant, by Certified Mail, a Notice of Rental Due letter. The above mentioned rental payment must be received by the BLM within 30 days from receipt of such notice, after which an oil and gas lease will be issued. An applicant is not required to pay the rental on any tract won.

**Figure 5-3**—BLM filing procedure.

*(Figure 5-3 continued on page 78)*

*(Figure 5-3 continued )*

**Miscellaneous Provisions:**

1. To receive an oil and gas lease, an applicant must be a U.S. citizen over 21 years of age.

2. An applicant may only file one Simultaneous Entry Card per tract. There is no limit on the number of tracts an applicant may file upon.

3. Each applicant must be the only party in interest in each application. A husband and wife may file a separate Simultaneous Entry Card on the same tract.

4. The cancelled Simultaneous Entry Card of an unsuccessful applicant is returned to the applicant by the BLM.

5. The drawing results are usually published by the BLM around the 10th to 15th of the month following the filings.

6. The number of acres covered by any one tract or oil and gas lease applicable thereto, ranges from a minimum of 40 acres to a maximum of 10,240 acres.

7. The BLM retains a royalty of 12.5% of gross production on any oil and gas lease issued.

8. To maintain any lease in force after the first year, an annual rental of $1 per acre must be paid to the BLM prior to the end of the first year and prior to the end of any subsequent year. The BLM will mail the leaseowner of record, approximately 30 days before due date, a statement of rental due, nonpayment of such rental results in the lease expiring.

9. The discovery of oil or gas in paying quantities will hold a lease past its expiration date.

---

with a number of calls from would-be purchasers with each vying to outbid the others. The normal result in this situation is for the lease holder (if it's not an oil company) to assign the lease to another party for a significant profit and an overriding royalty interest that assures him of some income from any oil or gas production. For the losers, there is a $10 write-off on their income tax for each entry, and an enhanced awareness that winning is a matter of luck, or just wait until next time.

Participation in the federal lottery allows a direct tax write-off and thus provides some consolation to the losers. At a later date, this tax write-off will provide an even greater consolation to the winners of the undesired land tracts.

In reading the results of a federal oil and gas lease lottery, it is evident that a few tracts draw a disproportionate amount of attention. These are the "plums," where available geological facts strongly suggest a greater-than-normal degree of oil or gas merit. There may be several thousand entries on each of the favored leases, and thus a single entry has only a slight hope of winning. The consoling factor is that all applicants have the same chance.

A number of consulting organizations are available to provide guidance for willing investors who cannot discriminate between possibly good and appallingly bad lease areas. The costs of this service vary, and no data are available to pass judgment on the result. However, they do provide a benefit, since they can dissuade an investor from committing funds to "goat pasture." The usual fee for this service is an added sum for their recommendation to each $10 filing fee.

Most leases won in state or federal lotteries have either negligible, or only very weak geological appeal. The winner of each lease is committed to pay the annual per-acre rental for the duration of the lease. The first rental payment is required—if the winner elects to accept the lease; nonpayment of subsequent rentals will result in forfeiture of the lease.

Federal filings are an inexpensive and sometimes rewarding approach for investing in the oil business. The two risks involved are the initial tract selection and the luck of the draw. A preference for which leases to apply for can be established by an expert on the region, but many investors would rather not incur this added expense.

Any U.S. citizen can participate in a federal filing. To obtain a copy of the BLM simultaneous drawing list and the results thereof, an individual must establish an account with each BLM office in which he might have an interest. It costs $5 per month to secure a copy of the postings and $4 per month for the drawing results. The addresses of the major BLM offices in the Rocky Mountain area are listed on the following page:

Wyoming:
   P. O. Box 1828
   Cheyenne, Wyoming 82001

Utah:
   136 E. South Temple
   Salt Lake City, Utah 84111

New Mexico:
   P. O. Box 1449
   Santa Fe, New Mexico 87501

Colorado:
   Room 700
   Colorado State Bank Building
   1600 Broadway
   Denver, Colorado 80202

Montana:
   P. O. Box 30157
   Billings, Montana 59107

## Who Is a Promoter?

In the oil business the term *promoter,* as commonly used, designates an individual who presents and negotiates deals. He may be an academically qualified professional, an astute business man, a dilettante, or even an inept bungler. It is an honorable and necessary service that he performs, and his occasional successes are amply punctuated with long strings of endless geological presentations and fruitless meetings. Most independent oilmen, petroleum geologists, and landmen are promoters at one time or another during their professional careers.

In his selling capacity the promoter is representing either himself or another person or group in the presentation of data relating to an oil or gas venture. The reward for his services may be a regular paycheck if he is employed in the land or exploration department of a large organization. If he is self-employed or has some informal working arrangement with an exploration group, he may receive a fee, commission, or royalty interest on what he sells.

Oil companies with their large technical staffs are continuously searching for new areas in which to seek oil and gas. The company that initiates a program frequently requires partners as exploration costs mount or when expensive drilling is anticipated. On rare occasions, partners are solicited on a ground floor basis, where the new entry in the program pays only their share of all previous and future costs and receives a proportionate share of the revenue interest. A true ground floor deal is normally available only at the inception of an idea. Deals that are consummated, in part or entirely, after the work has been started usually provide some promotional benefits to the seller. Frequently, the selling company will receive some cash beyond its costs, and some retained interests in the property. This interest may be in the form of an overriding royalty or possibly a back-in working interest after payout.

In selling a prospect the promoter will organize all lease, financial, and geological-geophysical data relating to the project. A dog and pony show is staged for the prospective buyer, frequently with various experts being brought in to embellish various facets of the deal. Technical strengths are pointed out, and weaknesses are explored. A single presentation may attract the necessary backer, or it may require contacting several dozen prospective partners before the deal is either sold or discarded.

The U.S. Securities and Exchange Commission defines a promoter as:

> ... (1) any person who, acting alone or in conjunction with one or more persons, directly or indirectly takes the initiative in founding and organizing the business or enterprise of the issuer; or (2) any person who, in connection with the founding or organizing of the business or enterprise of the issuer, directly or indirectly receives in

consideration of services or property, 10 percent or more of the proceeds from the sale of any class of securities. However, a person who receives such securities or proceeds either solely as underwriting commissions or solely in consideration of property shall not be deemed a promoter within the meaning of this paragraph if such person does otherwise take part in founding and organizing the enterprise.

This rigorous definition of a promoter deviates considerably from the common usage of the term in the oil business.

# Chapter Six

## The Scam

Few pedestrians would pause at night to heed a voice in a dark alley saying "Boy, have I got a deal for you. Just slip half your life savings, along with your business card under that brick near your foot, and I may make you rich. Incidentally, if I need more money, I'll send for it."

Calculated fraud in the oil business is generally more imaginative and sophisticated, but the net result is the same. Many people—some of whom would fight to their last drop of adrenelin to protect a billfold containing a few dollars, a charge card, and a driver's license—will enthusiastically turn over a significant portion of their accumulated savings on the basis of a charming and persuasive voice on the telephone.

### What Is Fraud?

The U.S. Securities and Exchange Commission (SEC) was established to function as a regulatory body with investigative powers to assure compliance in the purchase or sale of securities, with various provisions as set forth in the Securities Act of 1933, and the Securities Exchange Act of 1934.

In defining fraud the SEC employs a dictionary and a battery of lawyers. To the SEC, fraud is either a misapplication of investor funds or the misrepresentation or omission of data that precludes an investor from making a knowledgeable decision. The term "misapplication of funds" holds little mystery for an investor with an extravagant spouse. The misdirection of rent and grocery money has certainly contributed to the maintenance of some elegant race tracks and plush "fat farms."

In the oil and gas business misapplication focuses on the raising of funds for a specified purpose and then using all or a portion of those funds in a manner not intended by the investor. The fraudulent diversion of capital is the "game plan" for the nefarious operator. The amount and use of the money is curbed only by the moderation of his program and the limitation of his personal goals, respectively. Airplanes, fancy autos, and stunning arm adornments are popular items when playing with someone else's money.

One entrepreneur established his base of operations in Louisiana and proceeded to separate an estimated three hundred "clients" from the fluid portion of their capital. His misapplication centered on a high degree of access to company funds and the employment of a portion of these resources in fields not normally considered pertinent to the search for oil and gas. In the course of his operations he acquired an interest in two auto race tracks and managed to embellish his reputation as an inept businessman.

An adventurer in Oklahoma, along with some business associates and family members, demonstrated less flair in using diverted funds. They pocketed in excess of $250,000 and employed varying amounts in the purchase and maintenance of an airplane and in the investment of other organizations which they controlled. On the more frivolous side, they used diverted funds to pay for membership in an athletic club and to cover the costs of a home fire protection system.

The deliberate misrepresentation or omission of data to an investor is a constant companion of, and frequently the seed for, fraudulent enterprises. In the oil business an embellishment of an operator's success or the deliberate misstatement of a well's productivity are common enticements to an investor. With a little homework, however, these items can be verified, and certainly should be, prior to plundering the children's piggy banks. State agencies such as the Texas Railroad Commission; The Corporation Commission, Oklahoma; and The Office of Conservation, Louisiana; maintain accurate records with regard to wells drilled in the state and their ultimate outcome. To direct an inquiry to the Commission, it is necessary that you have the operator's name, the well name or names, and the portion of the state in which the drilling occurred. A few minutes' time spent in verifying a questionable claim can save money and embarrassment.

## How Are Fraudulent Oil and Gas Deals Sold?

Most fraudulent oil deals are discussed and consummated by telephone and mail with the buyer seldom exposed to the vendor. In some instances an acquaintanceship does exist between the two parties, which generally provides for an easier sale and no added burdens on the vendor's conscience.

When a sale is programmed, a common approach is to collect a force of experienced salespersons and to open a "boiler room." In this type of approach a number of phones are installed in the "operation center," with each phone having an assigned salesman with a "mullet" list and a "pitch" sheet. The mullet (potential client) list may be a Dunn & Bradstreet listing for a select occupation within a particular geographic area.

The pitch sheet is the sales presentation that has been prepared to assist the salesperson in sounding knowledgeable. The conversation will go something like this:

"Hello Charlie? This is (salesperson's name) with _____ Oil and Gas, Oklahoma City. Say Charlie, a few weeks ago I sent you some information on oil and gas wells, and I'm just following through to: number one, see if you got it and, number two, I don't have anything to sell you, but if you want anymore information I'll be happy to send it to you."

The person receiving this call provides the normal response such as:

1. Where did you get my name?
2. Yes, I did get it.
3. No, I did not get it.
4. I don't know if I received it or not.
5. It might be on my desk.

The pitchman then continues:

"Ok, let me tell you a little about what I'm doing here and, *if you want me to,* I'll be happy to send you more material. Charlie, I'm an independent oil operator, and I'm drilling oil and gas fields in Oklahoma. *I'm not wildcatting* because I'm going into proven fields that the majors used to be in. We are having a field day. We're hitting about 80% of these wells, but I want you to know right now it's still a gamble. It's just like going to a Las Vegas crap table. Of course, I think we have loaded dice. I've got a geologist, but I swear to God, I think he's a witch doctor."

"Well I'll tell you what I'll do, Charlie, *if you want me to,* I'll send you some more tax information and a standard _____ offering on a well that's been sold out. You can read it over and, *if you want me to,* I'll put your name on my list. If I ever get an opening, I'll give you a buzz, run it by you, and then it's up to you. If you want to roll the dice—Great! If you want to pass—that's fine too. Charlie, have a good day."

While the hook has not been taken at this stage, at least a degree of rapport and acquaintanceship has been established. As a follow-up to the initial conversation, there may be additional verbal exchanges and probably a write-up extolling the virtues of the drill site or sites. To emphasize the "good ole boy" association between the salesman and the victim, the salesman employs statements like:

"This well is going to be a barnburner, in fact we're parking our cars a quarter mile away cause we're afraid the ground's going to open up and swallow everything when this mother *comes in*" or "This is the best well I could put you in. Hotter than sliced bread. A barnburner. Gooder 'n snuff."

The pitch is often persuasive and always entertaining. A set of instructions to the salesmen in a separate venture urged them to initiate the conversation by creating the image of just having returned from the oil patch in their dust and oil-caked Cadillac. An aura of success is a definite asset in finding partners in an oil deal.

A much lower-key presentation used by another boiler room operation was as follows:

> Hello, _____ , I'm _____ with _____ . We are an independent oil and gas company, and I'm in the funding department.
>
> We're expanding our drilling operations to take advantage of the increasing demand for oil and gas. We'll also be expanding our investor group. I don't have anything I can offer you right now, but if you're interested I can send you some material on what we're doing.
>
> This business is *strictly* a gamble and anyone who risks his money in it should be prepared to lose. You can check with your accountant to see how this fits in with your tax situation.
>
> If you want me to, I'll send you some material on one of our leases. If I get an opening on one of these drilling programs, do you want me to give you a call? [Be sure to verify their mailing address.]

Included with this pitch were instructions to the salesman on topics not to discuss:

1. Present barrels per day
2. Estimate pay back period
3. Estimate when first production checks will be sent
4. Represent percentage of successful wells
5. Discuss tax benefits

The technical talents of the boiler room salesman in the oil and gas field seldom extends beyond the data sheet that his supervisor provides. If you are interested in the deal, get his name and number and have an expert question him.

## How Is Fraud Carried Out in the Oil Business?

"Now let me get this straight. You say that under one of those three shells is a $10,000 gold nugget, and I can pick one shell for $5 and a second shell for $50. Boy, the odds' are sure on my side...."

The simplest fraud in the oil business is to raise money for the drilling of a well and then not perform the required work. Everything is profit except the commission to salesmen, a telephone bill, and some printing costs. This type of program has a limited future, especially with the proliferation of state and federal agencies that oversee the oil business.

More commonly, funds are raised for a specified drilling program that may involve one to a dozen wells. The vehicle for obtaining the money will be a lease or leases and a report that broadly summarizes both the geology and the oil or gas production in the area. After some advertising, the operators of the program are awed by the inrush of funds. They begin to divert a portion of the money for their own personal use. Unsecured loans are floated from the company kitty, relatives are put on the payroll, and a grander personal lifestyle is embraced. The programmed wells are drilled, usually with a notable lack of success. The same flawed judgment that regulates their business activities spills over into their primary task of finding oil. Had they exercised more diligence in the selection of drill sites they likely would have spent less time consulting lawyers. A little success can counterbalance a lot of shortcomings.

One particular avenue of fraud that has been adapted in the oil business is the *Ponzi scheme,* named after an early practitioner. In this situation a promoter will approach a group of potential investors and encourage them to put up a sum of money that will be employed in "low-risk" drilling ventures. Because of the "certainty of success," he guarantees that at the end of three months (or possibly six months) they will receive X amount of profit and X amount of interest on their investment. This profit and interest will be forthcoming thereafter at regular intervals.

The promoter then approaches a second group of investors with the same spiel. A portion of the money received from the second group is then used to pay off what has been promised to the first group. Subsequent dealings may involve a third, fourth, or more groups. The bulk of the capital retained by the promoter may be employed, along with ample prayers, in drilling wells with the hope of establishing some equilibrium. This result seldom, if ever, occurs, and the budding financial talent, possibly in company with his creative accountant, are trapped in the rubble of the collapsing pyramid.

Another successful approach to gathering a little "spending money" is to oversell a drilling deal. Even with the application of modern math it is apparent that 100% represents everything, and anything beyond this quantity simply does not exist. The basic formula in a drilling deal might involve the selling of a 10% interest in a well to 20 different people. (Let's see: 10% x 20 = 200% Wow!) Each participant pays their proportionate share of all costs. A good promotional fee is directed back to the operator so that the investors will not think the deal is "too sweet" and thus be suspicious.

The drill site in this operation is selected with a great deal of care. An inadvertent, unplanned discovery, especially in front of witnesses, is a catastrophe for the promoter. The East Texas Field is the largest oilfield that has been found in the "original forty-eight." Its discoverer, "Dad" Joiner, through an unfortunate mathamatical calculation (addition) oversold the interest in the discovery well and adjoining leases. This problem was ultimately remedied by a patchwork of various deals and some nimble footwork.

Fraud is fraud, but the game sometimes strays beyond the bounds of normal comprehension. An especially unworthy approach for any self-respecting con man is to play the "widows game." In this operation close attention is paid to the obituary column in various newspapers. After a decent interval, a call is placed to the survivor, and a request is made to speak to the deceased. When informed of the circumstances, the caller pretends surprise and expresses profound sympathy. The caller then informs the widow that her late husband had expressed a great desire to be included in the next oil deal that became available through the caller's organization. The widow, frequently in need of guidance and wanting to cater to her late husband's last wishes, will agree to invest in the con man's program. The chances of success for the investor in this type of program are nil.

## How Does a "Wormy" Oil Deal Differ from Fraud?

A wormy deal is an oil investment scheme in which the intent is to defraud, but the program is executed in such a fashion that the motive cannot be proven. For example, a lease is obtained and a well is programmed. Interests are sold in the venture for an outrageous price, and the well is drilled. If the well is not drilled, it is fraud. If pertinent data are misrepresented in the raising of drilling funds, it is fraud whether the well is drilled or not.

The site selected for the well is one where oil or gas indications are common, although seldom representative of commercial deposits. This type of con artist prefers not to pay the lease cost to obtain acreage in an area that has genuine commercial oil or gas merit.

In any event, the well is drilled, and the encouraging oil and gas shows are reported to the investors, along with a request for additional funds. The needed money, again way beyond the necessary amount, is employed in "testing the first well and for the purchase of offsetting oil and gas leases."

Letters are periodically directed to the investors expressing cautious optimism for the first well, and the necessity to pursue this potential "hot find" with additional wells before "word gets around."

The investor has boarded an escalator where the degree of his financial involvement is repeatedly increased. It is difficult to step off, as mortals seldom have such business opportunities. However, this investment is not an escalator. It is a plummeting elevator where the controls are maintained by a glib con artist who will strip his descending passengers until they reach a jarring impact with reality.

A wormy deal sells because the sequence of events, beginning with an initial investment and followed by encouragement and more investment, is the pattern that many honest ventures follow. It is normal to expand your holding and increase your activity if an initial test well has highly encouraging shows.

When a question of operational integrity arises, the only legal alternatives for the investor are to get out of the deal or consult an expert.

## How Can an Expert Detect Fraudulent Intent in an Offering Circular?

Fraud cannot be detected on the basis of the information supplied in an offering circular. Factors such as unreasonable costs, poor geological concepts, a very unfavorable split in revenue interest, and the potential of unending contributions generally can be evaluated and should be used in abandoning a venture before the operator's ethics are tested.

The following excerpts are taken from a deal where investor money was collected, and the well was not drilled:

1.    _____ proposes to drill a well on a 20-acre tract located about 6 miles from _____ , Texas.

The amount of acreage is small, and thus the deal immediately loses some appeal.

2.    This is a three-year lease owned outright by _____ , together with options on an additional 470 acres surrounding this location. The landowner receives 12.5% of the production should the well be successful, and there are overriding

royalties amounting to an additional 12.5%, leaving 75% of the total production for working interests. The landowner and overriding royalty holders make no investments and participate in no maintenance or operating costs.

So far, everything is progressing in a normal manner. The lessor is entitled to a royalty of 12.5% on all revenues earned by the well. The promoter has elected to reward himself for his efforts with a revenue interest of 12.5% without any capital expenditures on his part.

At this point, a total of 25% of the potential earnings in the well have been accounted for. Let's see what happens to the remaining 75% of the possible earnings.

3.  This 75% of the production is divided into 100 equal nonproducing working interests. The offeror retains 34 of these and 66 are released to investors. Working interest holders participate on a pro-rata basis for maintaining and operating the well. The smallest fractional interest offered is 3/100 (3%) of 75% of the total production from the entire tract, and such interest will be entitled to one barrel of oil or one Mcf of gas out of every 44.3 barrels of oil and/or 44.3 Mcf of gas produced from the entire tract. No value is claimed for gas.

At this stage, "a little spin has been put on the ball," and the would-be investor has probably lost sight of just what percent of the revenue he will earn. The division between percent costs and percent potential revenue are in Table 6-1.

If the investor acquires the minimum working interest of 3%, he is liable for 3% of the costs and earns 2.25% of any revenues that develop.

4.  In the event the well is a commercial producer, or is unsuccessful but reveals prospects for an oil- or gas-bearing well at another location on the lease, subsequent well(s) will be drilled on the lease, and participants in the _____ #1 well shall have first right of refusal to participate in the next well(s)

### Table 6-1
### Costs vs. Potential Revenue

|  | Costs(%) | Potential Revenue(%) |
|---|---|---|
| Lessor | 0 | 12.5 |
| Promoter | 34 | (.34 x 75) + 12.5 = 38.0 |
| Investors | 66 | (.66 x 75)    = 49.5 |
|  | 100 | 100.0 |

so drilled. This right shall continue with all wells drilled on the lease by _____ unless interrupted by an investor's failure to exercise such right on one well, which will result in his forfeiture of any rights on the lease.

The investor is forewarned that the well may not be successful, *but* he will be given other opportunities for drilling on this skinny 20-acre lease. If he does not pay his share of future costs, he is out of the deal.

5.  The initial fixed price of $2610 for a 3% working interest pays for the drilling and testing of this one well to the casing point. If offeror is of the opinion that the well merits an attempt at completion, the 3% purchaser will pay an additional $2545, which will be the purchaser's fixed cost for completing and equipping the well into the tanks and ready for production. When the decision to complete has been made, offeror will invoice purchaser for completion costs, which are due and payable ten (10) days after invoice date. If payment is not received within (10) days after invoice date, Purchaser's interest in the lease and in this well, together with his drilling and testing payment, may be forfeited, at the option of offeror. Each interest is also chargeable with its pro-rata share of the operating and maintenance costs after the well has been placed on production. Such costs are estimated at $300 per month per well, or $9 for the minimum pro-rata share.

Ignore the cost figures, as this deal was circulated in 1975. By accepting this deal, the investor agrees to pay $2610 for a 3% working interest which equates to a 2.5% revenue interest. This $2610 payment is only for the drilling of the well to casing point (the point in time when a decision is made to either plug and abandon the well or to set casing in the hole and attempt to complete the well as an oil or gas producer).

If the information obtained during the drilling or as a result of logging is encouraging, the operator may elect to attempt a completion. If he does so, the investor is obligated to pay an additional $2545 for the 3% working interest or lose his interest in both the well and the lease. Few investors backout at this stage, so their financial commitment essentially doubles.

The operation and maintenance costs referred to in the last sentence of Section five are not unreasonable.

6. _____ will cause the well to be drilled as soon as it has been subscribed, but in any event no later than _____, to a depth of 3200 ft., or sufficient depth to test the Strawn sands at 1900, 2250, and 3100 feet.

7. Offeror has a contract for drilling this well at $38,190. To this have been added: $6000 lease cost, $500 legal fees, $750 travel, $3000 geological surveys, maps and drilling supervision, $9000 administrative and contingencies. Thus the total cost to investors for drilling and testing the well is $57,440.

At this stage the unscrupulous promoter has run up his flag, and it's a white skull and crossbones on a black field. In paragraph seven, the lease cost is listed as $6000, which nets out to $300 per acre on the 20-acre tract. This cost is ridiculous for the area in which the prospect is located. A cost of $50 per acre could assure the dealer a substantial profit.

Five hundred dollars won't approach the potential legal fees that he incurred in this operation. The travel cost, geological cost, etc. are blown completely out of proportion. The crowning insult

## Table 6-2
## Corrected Costs vs. Potential Revenue

|            | Costs(%) | Potential Revenue(%) |
|------------|----------|----------------------|
| Lessor     | 0        | 12.5                 |
| Promoter   | 0        | 38.0                 |
| Investors  | 100      | 49.5                 |
|            | 100      | 100.0                |

is that the well costs are $57,440 of which the promoter is supposed to pay 34% (paragraph three, lines two and three). By multiplying the 22 investors that have 3% each by their contribution (22 x 2610), the players who supposedly have only a 66% cost obligation are paying $57,420, or essentially the full well costs.

The cost and potential revenue table as shown previously should now be corrected as in Table 6-2.

8. Completion costs are estimated at $46,000. To this have been added: telephone $350, supervision $1500, travel $750, administrative and contingencies $6600, legal fees $800. Total estimated completion costs come to $56,000. As there is no assurance of the exact completion costs, offeror will bear any excess costs above the estimated $56,000. Any savings on the estimated $56,000 will be returned to investors on a pro-rata basis. The items added to the drilling and testing and completion costs represent 22% of the total amount paid by investors for a completed well.

With the general tenor of the deal, it appears at this stage that the investor's best interest could be served with a dry hole. The natural suspicion, however, is that encouraging shows will be found in the well and that a completion will be attempted. This work will in turn be followed by the necessity to drill offset sites, *ad nauseam*.

9.   There is no litigation pending. Offeror warrants that the lease
     is free and clear of any liens or indebtedness, and that
     _____ has no liens or debts against it. Under agreement
     with the drilling contractor, such funds will be released only to
     pay the costs involved in drilling and testing this well.

10.  Offeror proposes to use 20-acre spacing. The allowable is
     unknown, since the last well drilled near this location was in
     1955.

The 20-year span (1955-75) of inactivity in this area gives some
idea of its petroleum merit. Lease costs were likely from $5 to $20
per acre.

11.  This well will have to produce approximately 15,900 barrels of
     oil for the investor to realize a payout on his investment,
     without considering severance taxes or maintenance costs.
     Strawn sand oil is now selling for $12.50 per barrel.

12.  In the event this well is put into production, investors will sign
     a standard operating agreement with _____ (copy avail-
     able upon request). Offeror will furnish investors assignments
     of their interests duly filed and recorded in _____ County,
     Texas. Royalty payments will be made monthly to investors.
     The company which purchases the oil will deduct the
     appropriate severance taxes, and offeror will deduct opera-
     ting costs from each check and furnish a statement of same to
     investor.

13.  This private offering is made only to individuals who have had
     prior experience with oil and gas investments and who are
     therefore able to evaluate such prospects for themselves, and
     who can afford the financial loss should this well prove to be
     unproductive.

The preceding deal is real and was sold, although the well was
not drilled. The well was not drilled because one investor had the

hindsight, after paying his money, to check with a professional. The investor was advised to contact an attorney and the state and federal agencies that oversee such operations. The promoter made restitution with some hot checks and left the state.

# Chapter Seven

## The Feds

A number of federal agencies are either directly or indirectly involved with the oil and gas business. The Department of Energy (DOE), the Securities and Exchange Commission (SEC), and the Internal Revenue Service (IRS) all devote a significant portion of their time and personnel verifying that both the companies in the business and individuals associated therewith are fulfilling their legal obligations to the country and its citizens.

An investor in the oil and gas business is required to shoulder his share of the burdens and to accept full responsibility for his actions. In return, he is granted the legal benefits he deserves from his investment, and the assurance that efforts are being exerted continuously to reduce the nontechnical risks associated with the enterprise.

### What Is the Role of the SEC in the Oil Industry?

The SEC specifically classifies securities as either *registered* or *unregistered*. Each category requires the fulfillment of certain criteria and the submission of various data relating to the offering organization. Any transaction involving unregistered securities is further classified as either a public or private offering.

A private offering is a convenient vehicle employed by many operators in soliciting funds, usually from small investors, to carry out a drilling program. The advantage of such a program to the investor is the greater degree of personal involvement in the oil and gas business plus the potential of higher-than-usual profits. The disadvantage is the high risk it entails, including the wormy oil deals and fraud which are sometimes encountered.

The ability of an operator to provide a private offering for unregistered securities is based on the Securities Act of 1933, specifically Section 4, Subsection 2, as later clarified in Rule 146. In effect, this tongue twister defines the criteria that must be met to establish a private offering and which, when met, provide the operator the security of a safe harbor. Some of the criteria follow:

1. The sale of unregistered securities in a private offering must be restricted to 35 or fewer investors. Not included in this count is the investor whose involvement is in the amount of $150,000 or more.

2. Public solicitation (radio, television, newspapers, etc.) cannot be employed in enlisting investors.

3. The investor must be sophisticated in the field of the proposed investment or utilize the expertise of an uninvolved third party who is knowledgeable in the field of the proposed investment.

With the previous restrictions, the operator is limited to contacting only a few parties and then either in person, on the telephone, or through the mail. Any expression of interest by a would-be participant will result in his being forwarded an offering circular.

The SEC then requires that certain statements be made and that specific conditions be fulfilled within the circular (SEC Rule 256):

These securities are offered pursuant to an exemption from registration with the *United States* securities and exchange commission. The commission does not pass upon the merits of any securities nor does it pass upon the accuracy or completeness of any offering circular or other selling literature.

The format of offering circulars is therefore broadly similar, with some modifications because of state requirements. The heart of the circular, and where it receives its character, is the projected program, its costs, merits, and possible rewards.

The SEC's involvement in an oil or gas drilling program is commonly prompted by an investor or group of investors who believe that the operations are not being conducted along the agreed-upon lines. At this stage, the damage has been done, and the value of an investigation is primarily in curtailing any future fraudulent activities. The refund of investor funds is uncommon, as these resources are usually depleted at that time. In addition, many investors prefer to write off the loss rather than have their bad business judgment aired.

When fraud is established, there is a collective crash of collapsing dreams (both the investors' and the promoter's). An unscrupulous operator, brought to heel in one state, will frequently ford a river, change the company name, reactivate his mullet list, and continue business as usual. It's hard to break a "chicken-chasing dog" of his favorite pastime, especially when he's hungry.

Initial contact in many small investor oil and gas deals is established by telephone. The potential investor should observe the following procedure if he is indeed interested in the venture:

1. Note the saleman's name, phone number, and his company's name.

2. If the firm name is not familiar, contact both the State and U.S. Government Securities and Exchange office, and request any information that they can provide concerning the organization. Specifically inquire about data from their SV (Securities Violations) file. Additional information can be obtained about the organization under the

Freedom of Information Act (FOIA) but will require some paperwork on the potential investor's part.

3. If the pending investment still has a "green light," contact a professional (petroleum geologist, petroleum landman, petroleum engineer), and proceed with an economic and technical analysis.

## What Are the Tax Advantages of an Oil Deal?

An investor's primary motive for participating in oil and gas ventures is not always clear. Although federal income tax benefits are alluring, an investor should not let such tax benefits overshadow all other considerations. A wise investor will seek competent professional advisors who can evaluate a prospective venture in terms of its own merits. Tax benefits can only soften the blow of a bad deal; the investor still loses money. Entering an oil deal for tax advantages is like entering a beauty contest to win Miss Congeniality.

A tax-sheltered investment possesses one or more of the following traits:

1. Income derived from the investment is wholly or partially tax-free (e.g. municipal bonds)

2. Income recognition is deferred to later tax years (e.g. installment sales arrangements)

3. Tax deduction recognition is accelerated to earlier tax years (e.g. accelerated depreciation on buildings)

The shelter aspect of oil and gas ventures is that tax deductions are accelerated; 70-80% of the initial investment is ordinarily deductible in the first year. *Intangible drilling costs* (IDC), the primary income tax advantage of an oil and gas investment, constitute roughly 70% or more (almost 100% for dry wells) of all costs incurred in a successful drilling operation. The IDC represents labor, material, equipment rental, and other related costs associated with a drilling operation. The benefits of IDC provide the dominant incentive for investment in oil and gas for most individual taxpayers in the 50-70% tax bracket.

Expenditures for items such as production casing, wellhead assembly, tanks, pumps, and other similar equipment that have useful lives of more than one year are classified as *tangible* (or capital) *costs* and, as such, are subject to both depreciation and investment tax credit. Generally, investment tax credit provides a dollar-for-dollar reduction in income tax liability in the amount of 10% of such costs during the year of purchase, assuming the purchases have a useful life of seven years or more. Depreciation (a noncash deduction) is recoverable over the useful life (commonly 7-10 years) of the assets. In addition, accelerated methods may be used which provide for greater "up-front" deductions. Normal repairs and maintenance associated with the equipment may simply be expensed.

Another substantial income tax benefit, the *depletion deduction,* is earned when an investor or royalty owner receives income from production. The depletion deduction was created to provide an allowance for many natural resources, such as oil and gas, which are categorized as *wasting assets.* Cost depletion refers to the write off of capitalized acquisition and/or drilling costs associated with producing properties. Generally, the allowance is determined by multiplying these costs by the ratio of actual yearly production (in units) to estimated reserves. For example, if depletable costs are $10,000, and 500 barrels and 10,000 barrels are annual production and estimated reserves, respectively, then cost depletion for the year amounts to ($10,000 x 500) ÷ 10,000 = $500.

*Statutory* (or percentage) *depletion* provides a deduction of 22% of gross income earned from oil and gas revenues. Generally, statutory depletion is not allowable to an individual where production exceeds 1000 barrels of oil or the equivalent gas production daily. In addition, statutory depletion is determined on a property-by-property basis and cannot exceed 50% of an individual's taxable income from that particular property. Furthermore, percentage depletion cannot exceed 65% of taxpayer's total taxable income for the year.

The enactment of *The Crude Oil Windfall Profit Tax Act of 1980* ("the Act") has resulted in an unfavorable, industry-wide response. Industry experts view the decontrol of oil prices as an incentive for greater activity and investment in the oil and gas business, ultimately leading to the development of new reserves. It is recognized that the development of new fields will have little impact on reducing foreign crude oil imports as long as current rates of U.S. consumption are maintained. New, domestic oil reserves are required to offset dwindling production and to minimize the dependence on foreign supplies until alternative energy resources are developed. Energy is survival, and oil is the current key.

The "windfall profits" tax is an excise tax levied on any revenues realized above an established base price. There are two important factors in the tax structure: the varying price schedules that exist for different *tiers* of oil, and whether the oil is classified as "old" or "new." A complete discussion of these regulated price limits for different oil categories is beyond the scope of this guide.

An investor now entering the business and having the good fortune to be associated with an oil discovery is governed by the requirements pertaining to Tier 3 oil. This category encompasses newly discovered oil, heavy oil, and incremental tertiary oil. The first category, which relates to a new discovery, involves oil production from onshore fields or sites from which no oil was produced during 1978. An exception to this ruling is a new discovery within a 1978 producing area related to differing geological conditions, such as a deeper producing reservoir.

Heavy oil, for windfall profits tax purposes, is defined as having a weighted average gravity of 16.0 degrees API or less, corrected to 60°. As discussed in Chapter 1, degrees API is the standard measure for expressing the density of a crude oil. High-degree API values are characteristic of the highly volatile, light oils, while low values reflect the greater density, high-viscosity oils.

Incremental tertiary oil is defined as enhanced oil recovery from a reservoir because of the application of special mechanical or chemical techniques. The Department of Energy specifies that to qualify for crude oil decontrol an oil well or field must reach a level of production that is uneconomic prior to tertiary treatment. This increased increment of production thus developed is decontrolled, and therefore subject to a Tier 3 categorization.

The windfall profits tax requirements that cover most small investors in the oil and gas business relate to Tier 3 oil. The tax rate for this Tier is placed at 30%, with the base price at $16.55 per barrel (with inflation adjustments). Some consideration is also provided for oil quality and transport difficulties.

# Chapter Eight

# $ The Summary

Oil deals will continue to be constructed, explained, argued over, bought, sold, rejected, modified, and laughed at as long as the economic incentives exist to warrant the search for oil and gas. Participants in these ventures will experience agony, ecstasy, frustration, wealth, poverty, and occasional heartburn, with the number and variety of sensations depending on their frequency of exposure to the *mal de petrole*.

There are good, bad, indifferent, great, terrible, and crooked deals. The proper adjective is not contingent on the outcome of a venture, as the agreement itself is usually consummated before a well is drilled. A good deal can be broadly defined as one that is in a clear and acceptable format and provides reasonable economics and an accurate appraisal of risk.

If there is a golden rule that should be followed by all investors, big or small, knowledgeable or unknowledgeable, it is: *KNOW WITH WHOM YOU ARE DOING BUSINESS.* An investor is in jeopardy with an inept partner and in deep trouble with a crooked one. Check the credentials of an operator before signing on the dotted line. Ask for references, talk to previous investors, check with the SEC, or employ a consultant. This point is essential as all other factors are meaningless if you are involved with a bad faith partner.

The following list contains some indicators that may frequently point to an operator's ethical shortcomings:

1.  If the working interest and corresponding revenue interest of a deal are not prominantly and clearly stated, the operator himself likely has some misgivings about the equity of his terms. A data or summary sheet should be included in an offering circular that tells when, where, and how deep a well will be drilled. In addition, it should clearly state the costs to the investor and the working interest and revenue interest earned by this payment. If the revenue interest differs before and after payout, the reason and effect of this change should be made apparent to the investor.

2.  If a program is advertised as development or infield, be especially wary of investing. *Economically sound* programs of this nature are not usually available to anyone except relatives of the operator.

3.  Excessive lease and drilling costs can generate large profits for an unscrupulous operator, even when his program results in a series of dry holes or marginal producers. These figures are difficult for a nonprofessional to check on and thus it is advised that a consultant be employed to verify the reliability of costs.

There remains a great deal of oil and natural gas to be found and fortunes to be made and lost in the search. People will continue to invest in the business as it combines three factors that most mortals find irresistable: risk, income tax incentives, and the potential of sudden and significant wealth. It's a healthy pastime if pursued judiciously and within one's means. If only a single word of advice can be passed on to a nonprofessional oil investor, it should be to hire an expert for the necessary hour or day required to review the data before a deal is consummated. A petroleum geologist or engineer knowledgeable of the region where the program is to take place can provide an economic and technical evaluation that will cover all facets of the program and at a cost that is minor to the amount of the proposed investment. He cannot warrant success but can provide assurances that the program is conceptually sound, reasonably priced, and provides good, risk-weighed economic incentives for the investor.

# Recommended Reading

1. Bedford, E.M., "Leases, Concessions, Options, Permits," *Petroleum Exploration Handbook,* McGraw-Hill Book Co., 1961, pp. 16-1 to 16-21.
2. Beebe, B.W., "Drilling the Exploratory Well," *Petroleum Exploration Handbook,* McGraw-Hill Book Co., 1961, pp. 17-1 to 17-36.
3. Brantly, J.E., *History of Oil Well Drilling,* Gulf Pub. Co., 1971.
4. Campbell, J.L.P., "Radioactive Well Logging," *Petroleum Exploration Handbook,* McGraw-Hill Book Co., 1961, pp. 20-1 to 20-40.
5. Carter, F.B. and Whitaker, M.T., "Economic Analysis of Exploratory Projects," *Petroleum Exploration Handbook,* McGraw-Hill Book Co., 1961, pp. 14-1 to 14-12.
6. Chapman, R.E., *Petroleum Geology, A Concise Study,* Elsevier Scientific Pub. Co., 1976.
7. Clark, N.J., *Elements of Petroleum Reservoirs,* Society of Petroleum Engineers, Dallas, TX, 1969.
8. Dickey, P.A., *Petroleum Development Geology,* Petroleum Pub. Co., 1979.
9. Doll, H.G. et al, "Electrical Logging," *Petroleum Exploration Handbook,* McGraw-Hill Book Co., 1961, pp. 19-1 to 19-44.
10. Dyk, K., "Geophysical Surveys," *Petroleum Exploration Handbook,* McGraw-Hill Book Co., 1961, pp. 11-1 to 11-45.

11. Hilchie, D.W., *Applied Open Hole Log Interpretation,* D.W. Hilchie, Inc., 1978.
12. Lee, H.W., "Exploration Personnel," *Petroleum Exploration Handbook,* McGraw-Hill Book Co., 1961, pp. 3-1 to 3-7.
13. Loomis, F.B., "Subsurface Geology," *Petroleum Exploration Handbook,* McGraw-Hill Book Co., 1961, pp. 13-1 to 13-74.
14. Mayer-Gurr A., *Petroleum Engineering* (Geology of Petroleum, Vol. 3), John Wiley & Sons, 1976.
15. McCray, A.W. and Cole, F.W., *Oil Well Drilling Technology,* Univ. of Oklahoma Press, 1976.
16. Megill, R.E., *An Introduction to Exploration Economics,* Petroleum Pub. Co., 1971.
17. Millison, C., "Coring," *Petroleum Exploration Handbook,* McGraw-Hill Book Co., 1961, pp. 18-1 to 18-10.
18. Pearson, A.J., "Miscellaneous Well Logs," *Petroleum Exploration Handbook,* McGraw-Hill Book Co., 1961, pp. 21-1 to 21-30.
19. Robertson, J. *ABC's of Oil,* Petroleum Publishers, 1953.
20. Scoper, V. Jr., *Come Drill a Well in My Back Yard,* Laurel, MS, 1971.
21. Sheldon, D.H., "Petroleum Reservoirs," *Petroleum Exploration Handbook,* McGraw-Hill Book Co., 1961, pp. 7-1 to 7-16.
22. Skinner, D.R., *Introduction to Petroleum Production, Vols. 1-3,* Gulf Pub. Co., 1981.
23. Tiratsoo, E.N., *Oilfields of the World, 2nd ed.,* Gulf Pub. Co., 1976.
24. Tissot, B.P. and Welte, D.H., *Petroleum Formation and Occurrence: A New Approach to Oil and Gas Exploration,* Springer-Verlag, 1978.
25. Webber, C.E., "Estimation of Petroleum Reserves Discovered," *Petroleum Exploration Handbook,* McGraw-Hill Book Co., 1961, pp. 25-1 to 25-25.
26. Weeks, L.G., "Origin, Migration, and Occurrence of Petroleum," *Petroleum Exploration Handbook,* McGraw-Hill Book Co., 1961, pp. 5-1 to 5-50.
27. Wheeler, R.R. and Whited, M., *Oil From Prospect to Pipeline, 4th ed.,* Gulf Pub. Co., 1981.
28. Willis, D.G., "Entrapment of Petroleum," *Petroleum Exploration Handbook,* McGraw-Hill Book Co., 1961, pp. 6-1 to 6-68.

# Glossary

ABANDONMENT PRESSURE. Flowing pressure below which a gas well can no longer economically deliver gas to the surface.

ACIDIZE. The application of acid under high pressure to perforations in the carbonate formation to be tested.

AUTHORIZATION FOR EXPENDITURE (AFE). An estimate of well costs, broken down into different categories, that is provided by the operator to the participants prior to the initiation of the well.

BACK-IN. A working interest or revenue interest that is gained at the time a well or venture has achieved payout.

BAREFOOT COMPLETION. See *Open hole completion*.

BLOWOUT. An uncontrolled flow of fluid or gas from a borehole that occurs when mud weight is inadequate to control formation pressures.

BOILER ROOM. A high-pressure telephone sales operation in which potential clients (mullets) are selected on the basis of income and profession and tabulated alphabetically, i.e., the mullet list. The sales people in the operation follow a prepared speech (a pitch sheet) in the sales presentation to the potential customers.

BONUS. Cash payment, usually on a per-acre basis, to lessor in return for oil and gas lease.

BOTTOMS UP. To discontinue drilling yet maintain circulation of the mud system until the most recent cuttings reach the surface.

BRIDGE. Barrier in wellbore caused by accumulation of sidewall cavings.

CALIPER. Logging device that indicates the variation in hole diameter with depth.

CASED HOLE. A well in which the drilling has been completed and where a continuous conduit of tubular steel has been set from the surface down to the depth to be tested.

CAVINGS. Rock fragments dislodged from the well wall during drilling operations.

CIRCULATION. Continuous cycling of drilling mud between the drill bit and the surface

COMPLETION COSTS.    All material and personnel expenses that are incurred following the final open hole logging and directed toward establishing a well as an oil or gas producer. Principal cost items include production casing, cement, cased hole logging, formation treatment including fracturing, rig time, wellhead equipment, and service fees.

CONDENSATE.    Highly volatile, high-gravity liquid hydrocarbon with appearance of naphtha or gasoline.

CORE.    Cylindrical column of rock cut by a special bit and retained in a core barrel until brought to the surface.

CUBIC FEET.    Standard volumetric unit of measure for natural gas within the United States.

CUT.    The release of oil from rock chips or fragments by the application of an organic solvent. The presence and magnitude of a cut is usually determined by viewing the treated sample under ultraviolet light.

CUTTINGS.    Rock chips or fragments broken and dislodged by the drill bit and transported to the surface by the mud system.

DAY RATE.    Drilling costs based on a fixed fee for each 24 hours of operation.

DEPLETION ALLOWANCE.    Percentage of oil and gas production that is not subject to U.S. income tax.

DEVELOPMENT WELL.    A well drilled at a location of established merit based on the results of wells drilled nearby.

DISTILLATE.    Highly volatile, high-gravity liquid hydrocarbon with the appearance of naphtha or gasoline that is obtained through refining techniques.

DOG-LEG.    A sudden change in direction in a borehole.

DOWN TIME.    Time lost during drilling operation as a result of equipment problems or bad weather.

DRILL STEM TEST (DST).    Procedure whereby a test instrument with pressure recorder is attached to the drill pipe and lowered into the borehole. Information relating to formation fluid, pressure, and permeability is obtained.

DRILL STRING.    The continuous column of drill pipe utilized in the drilling of a well.

DRILLING BREAK.    A speeding up in the rate of drilling that frequently results from the drill bit encountering rocks of improved porosity or permeability.

DRY AND ABANDONED (D&A).   A well that is considered nonproductive and has had cement plugs set in the wellbore prior to abandonment.

DRY GAS.   Natural gas composed primarily of methane with no associated liquid hydrocarbons.

DRYHOLE COSTS.   All costs (exclusive of completion charges) related to a drilling operation from its inception up to and including the logging and plugging of a well and subsequent site restoration.

EXCESS ROYALTY.   Lessor royalty in an amount greater than 12.5%.

EXPLORATIONIST.   An individual who seeks oil or gas deposits and employs widely acceptable techniques in the search.

FARMOUT AGREEMENT.   A contractural agreement between two or more parties whereby one or more parties agree to undertake a specified exploration and/or drilling program for an agreed upon interest in property or leases held by the remaining party or parties. (Sometimes also referred to as a *Farmin Agreement, Sublease Agreement, Sharing Agreement.*)

FAULTING.   The breakage and separation of rock bodies caused by the unequal distribution of pressures within the earth.

FEE OWNERSHIP. The ownership of the surface and the mineral rights on a property.

FILTRATE.   Drilling fluid from which clay and other solids have been removed.

FISH.   To attempt recovery of equipment or material accidentally lost in a wellbore.

FLUORESCENCE.   Characteristic glow given off by hydrocarbons and various minerals when exposed to ultraviolet light.

FOLDING.   The bending of rock bodies caused by the unequal distribution of pressures within the earth.

FOOTAGE RATE.   Drilling costs based on a fixed fee for each foot of hole drilled.

GAS CAP.   A rock body in which the pore spaces contain a significant percent of gas by volume and which directly overlies a zone in which the pore spaces contain a significant percent of oil by volume.

GAS CUT MUD.   Gas-bearing drilling fluid recovered in testing or detected in mud stream.

GAS DRIVE RESERVOIR.   Reservoir wherein oil is displaced and transported up the wellbore to the surface by the expansion of natural gas.

GAS-OIL RATIO (GOR).    The relationship between cubic feet of gas and barrels of oil being produced from a well at a given time.

GROUND FLOOR.    Working interest participation on a non-promoted basis.

HYDROCARBON.    A compound with hydrogen and carbon as its elemental constituents.

INFIELD WELL.    See *Development well*.

INTANGIBLE DRILLING COSTS (IDC).    Charges for services and the purchase of expendable material during well drilling and completion operations.

ISOPACH.    A map designed to indicate the variation in thickness of a rock body over a given area.

JOINT.    A single section of drill pipe, casing, or tubing.

JUNKED AND ABANDONED (J&A).    A well that has been abandoned after cement plugs are placed in it. Abandonment is caused by the inability to continue drilling due to either the unfavorable condition of the hole or because debris (junk) is lodged in the hole and cannot be removed.

KELLY.    Hollow, 40-foot long, square or hexagonal stem connected to drill pipe and turned by rotary table during drilling.

KICK.    Abrupt displacement of mud in the wellbore due to the passage of gas to the surface.

LAG TIME.    Length of time required for cuttings to be transported by the mud system from the bottom of the hole to the surface.

LESSEE.    Recipient of an oil and gas lease.

LESSOR.    Conveyor of an oil and gas lease.

LOST CIRCULATION.    Fluid loss during drilling operations caused by the presence of high permeability in the formation being penetrated. This permeability is a result of either extensive fracturing or an unusually high development of porosity in the formation.

METHANE.    The simplest hydrocarbon compound. It may have either an organic or inorganic origin and is present in varying quantities in all liquid or gaseous hydrocarbon deposits.

MUD CAKE.    Clay and additives that constitute the solids in a drilling mud. A mud cake will form on a permeable rock surface as a residue when fluid from the mud passes into a formation. In logging operations the presence of a mud cake is interpreted as a permeability indicator.

MUD LOG.   This log is used in many drilling operations to provide a continuous analysis of the mud as it is circulated from the bottom of the drill hole to the surface. The logger records the rock types encountered at different drilling depths and all indications of hydrocarbons observed in either the mud system or the well cuttings. The drilling rate is usually determined and plotted by the mud logger.

MUD PIT.   All excavations at a drill site that are designed as part of the drilling fluid circulation and storage system.

MUD WEIGHT.   The weight in pounds of one gallon of drilling mud. Various additives will be introduced into a mud to increase its weight and minimize the risk of a blow out.

MULLET LIST.   See *Boiler room.*

NATURAL GAS.   The four primary constituents of the paraffin group of hydrocarbons. In order of increasing molecular complexity they are methane, ethane, propane and butane.

NET REVENUE INTEREST.   Percentage of the total revenue to be earned by an investor in a venture.

OFFERING CIRCULAR.   Written proposal outlining a drilling venture in which participants are sought. A discussion of cost, risk, profit potential, and geologic merit are commonly included in the write up.

OIL.   General term for liquid hydrocarbons.

OIL CUT MUD (OCM).   Drilling mud with a visible show of oil.

OIL GRAVITY (degree API).   An arbitrarily devised unit of measure that provides an expanded scale when comparing the density of different oils at 60°F.

OIL POOL.   A rock body in which the pore spaces contain enough oil for it to be extracted in commercial quantities.

OIL SHALE.   A very fine-grained sedimentary rock containing a significant percentage of extractable hydrocarbons.

OPEN HOLE COMPLETION.   Casing set above an anticipated reservoir with the hole then deepened to the depth to be tested.

OPERATOR. Individual or company responsible for all decisions relating to the drilling, testing, and completion of a well.

OVERRIDING ROYALTY INTEREST (ORRI).   A percentage of all revenue earned by a well and carrying no cost obligation.

PACKER.   A tool that attaches to the drill pipe that can be expanded to temporarily seal off a portion of a hole.

PAYOUT.    When the amount of money earned by the investors in a well from oil or gas revenue is equal to the cumulative cost.

PERFORATE.    Charges fired into the casing wall at preselected depths to establish conduits between the formation and casing.

PERMEABILITY.    The ability of a rock unit to transmit fluids.

PERMEABILITY BARRIER.    A vertical or lateral change in rock character that restricts or halts the passage of fluids.

PETROLEUM.    Naturally occurring liquid hydrocarbon that may contain varying degrees of impurities.

PITCH SHEET.    See *Boiler room*.

PLUG BACK (PB).    To seal off lower part of cased or open hole.

PLUGGED AND ABANDONED (P&A).    A well that is considered non-productive and has had cement plugs set in the wellbore prior to abandonment.

POROSITY.    The percentage volume of a rock body occupied by voids or pores. A measure of the storage capability of a reservoir for fluids.

PROMOTER.    An intermediary in an oil deal that sells participation in a venture and receives a salary, bonus, or interest in the program.

REENTRY.    A previously abandoned well that has had the plugs removed and is being subjected to additional drilling, testing, or other operations.

RESERVES, ESTIMATED.    The quantity of oil or gas contained within a volume of rock as estimated by assuming the value of variables such as reservoir volume and water saturation.

RESERVE PIT.    An excavation at a drill site to provide storage space for drilling fluids. See *Mud pit*.

RESERVES, PROVEN.    A determination of oil or gas in place within a specific formation and over a designated area.

RESERVOIR.    Rock body having adequate porosity and permeability to produce oil or gas.

REVENUE INTEREST.    The percentage of the total oil and gas earnings from a well to be gained by an investor.

ROUND TRIP.    The complete removal and subsequent reentry of all drill pipe in a well. Commonly associated with a change in bit or logging or testing operations.

ROYALTY.    A percentage of all oil and gas revenue from a well with no cost obligation.

SHOW. An indication of oil or gas in a well. An oil show may range from visible oil in the cuttings to more subtle indications such as fluorescence and cut.

SIDEWALL CORE (SWC). Rock sample obtained by firing core barrel into well wall.

SOUR CRUDE. An unrefined oil in which the content of sulfur compounds is greater than 0.5% by weight.

SPECIFIC GRAVITY. Weight of a substance compared to the weight of an equal volume of water.

SPUD. The initiation of drilling operations at a well site.

SQUEEZE. Pumping cement behind the casing under high pressure to seal off poorly cemented channeled or non-productive zones.

STRATIGRAPHIC TRAP. A permeability barrier within a rock body caused by the lateral and vertical transition of one rock type to another.

STAND. Two or three connected joints of drill pipe; as they are stored upright in the derrick.

STEP-OUT. A location offsetting a producing well that, if successful, will increase the size of a field.

STRUCTURAL TRAP. A barrier to the passage of fluids within a sequence of rocks caused by either folding or faulting.

STRUCTURE CONTOUR MAP. A presentation designed to indicate the configuration of the surface of a rock body and the depth at which it is found.

SUITCASE SAND. A term employed in the past to describe the deepest productive zone being sought in an area. If no oil or gas were found in the zone, the oil men and promoters packed their suitcases and left town.

SWAB. Rubber disc lowered and raised by wire line in a cased hole to provide lift and suction for removal of fluids.

SWEET CRUDE. An unrefined oil in which the content of sulfur compounds is less than 0.5% by weight.

TANGIBLE DRILLING COSTS. Charges that relate to the acquisition of capitalized equipment in the drilling, completion, or production operations on a well.

TAR SAND. A sandstone in which the pore spaces are filled with a highly viscous oil (tar).

TITE (TIGHT) FORMATION.    A rock body characterized by low permeability.

TOMBSTONE LIMESTONE.    A limestone with very low permeability and characterized by very high resistivity on electric logs.

TOOL PUSHER.    Drilling contractor employee who is responsible for maintaining a satisfactory level of performance by the drilling crews.

TOTAL DEPTH (TD).    Drilling depth reached in a bore hole.

TRAP.    A barrier that severely restricts the passage of oil or gas from one zone in a rock body to another.

TREND WELL.    A test located along the inferred projection of a producing belt.

TRIP GAS.    Gas that accumulated in the mud during operations involving the removal and later reentry of the drill pipe in the bore hole.

TURNKEY JOB.    The performance of specified services for a fixed price.

WATER DRIVE RESERVOIR.    An oil reservoir wherein the continued movement of water provides the necessary driving force to displace oil and to transport it into a well bore. The movement of this subsurface water may be either natural or amplified by the injection of large quantities of water into the reservoir at selected sites.

WATER SATURATION.    The percentage of a rock's volume occupied by water.

WELL.    Borehole that produces water, oil, or gas.

WELL LOG.    The recording in a sequential manner of data obtained from a well. Such data may consist of rock type determined from cuttings, or the electrical or physical properties of a rock body as determined by electrical or mechanical means.

WET FORMATION.    Reservoir that contains too large a quantity of water to allow oil or gas to be commercially produced.

WET GAS.    Natural gas with associated condensate.

WILDCAT.    A well that is either geographically or geologically disassociated from a producing well.

WIRE LINE.    Cable used to lower and raise various devices in a well bore.

WORKING INTEREST.    The percentage of the total program cost that is paid by an investor.

# Index

## A

AAPL. *See* American Association of Petroleum Landmen.
Abandonment (well), 12
Acid frac. *See* Fracturing.
Acoustic velocity log, 61
AFE. *See* Authorization for Expenditures.
Agreement (oil and gas), 22 ff.
American Association of Petroleum Landmen (AAPL), 73
Anticline, 15
Authorization for Expenditures (AFE) form, 70-73

## B

Back-in, 25, 45
Bargaining, 22 ff.
Barrels (to gallons), 14
Basal Conglomerate, 14
BLM. *See* Bureau of Land Management.
Bioherm, 14
Bit (drill), 54,56

Bitumens, 3
Blowout preventer (BOP), 56-57
Boiler room, 85
Bore (well), 56, 63
Break (drilling), 64
Butane, 5
Bureau of Land Management (BLM) lottery filing procedure, 76-80

## C

Cap, 5
Cap rock, 15
Carbonate rock, 67
Carbon Tetrachloride, 58
Cased hole logging, 59
Casing, 63, 66-67
Charges. *See* Costs.
Checkerboard, 45
Claim verification, 85
Coal, 8
Collar (drill), 55-56
Completion (well), 62-63
Condensate, 4
Consultant, 17, 19, 26, 105
Coring, 63-65
Corporation Commission. *See* Oklahoma.

Oil. *Also see* Oil and gas.
API values, 103-104
enhanced recovery, 104
formation of, 2
heavy, 103-104
incremental tertiary, 104
light, 103-104
new, 103
old, 103
pool, 4
recovery, 6
shales, 3-4
tiers, 103
windfall profits tax, 103-104
Oil and gas
agreement, 22 ff.
deal, 22 ff.
deposit, 11
entrapment. *See* Trap.
formation of, 2
geology of, 5-12
lease, 41 ff.
regulations, 23
reserve estimates, 20
reservoir, 20
rights, 27
search for, 9-12
seeps, 9
sour, 4
sweet, 4
Oklahoma
Corporation Commission, 85
mineral rights, 30
One-eighth. *See* Royalties.
Open hole logging, 31
Operations (drilling), 70-71
Operator, 18, 31, 69-73
Overriding royalty interest,
33-38

# P

Pad, (drilling), 16
Packer, 65
Paraffin, 5
Percentage depletion, 102
Perforating gun, 66-67
Permeability, 4, 62
Personnel (oil and gas), 69-82
Pinchout, 14
Pipe (drill), 54-56
Plugged back total depth (PB,
    PBTD), 51
Ponzi scheme, 88
Porosity, 4, 60-61
Pressure changes, 65
Pricing (oil), 103-104
Production casing, 63
Productive zones, 10, 13
Program (drilling), 12
Profit potential, 23, 29-32
Promoter, 18, 25, 36, 38, 80-82
Propane, 5
Propping agent, 68
Prospectus (drilling), 19

# R

"Race to the courthouse states,"
    44
Recoverable reserves, 19
Recovery (oil and gas), 6
Re-entry (well), 12-13, 16
Regions (oil and gas), 10-13
Reports
    investor, 70